DU311 Earth in crisis

Prospects and Possibilities

At The Open University we are committed to protecting the environment and to the responsible use of natural resources. We are acting on this commitment by working with paper suppliers and printers to phase out the use of paper produced from ancient and endangered forests. We aim to ensure that all paper products we purchase are derived from environmentally and socially responsible sources.

Text paper used is Precision Matt Blade paper manufactured at the Grycksbo paper mill in Sweden. Cover board is Trucard Duo Matt manufactured at the Tullis Russell board mill in Scotland. Both paper and board contain pulp sourced from forests independently certified to the Forest Stewardship Council (FSC) principles and criteria. Chain of custody certification allows the pulp from these forests to be tracked to the end use (see www.fsc.uk.org).

DU311 Earth in crisis

Prospects and Possibilities

Edited by Petr Jehlička and Philip Sarre

This publication forms part of an Open University course DU311 *Earth in crisis: environmental policy in an international context*. Details of this and other Open University courses can be obtained from the Student Registration and Enquiry Service, The Open University, PO Box 197, Milton Keynes MK7 6BJ, United Kingdom: tel. +44 (0)845 300 60 90, email general-enquiries@open.ac.uk

Alternatively, you may visit the Open University website at http://www.open.ac.uk where you can learn more about the wide range of courses and packs offered at all levels by The Open University.

To purchase a selection of Open University course materials visit http://www.ouw.co.uk, or contact Open University Worldwide, Walton Hall, Milton Keynes MK7 6AA, United Kingdom for a brochure. tel. +44 (0)1908 858793; fax +44 (0)1908 858787; email ouw-customer-services@open.ac.uk

The Open University
Walton Hall, Milton Keynes
MK7 6AA

First published 2009

Edited and designed by The Open University.

Typeset in India by Alden Prepress Services, Chennai.

Printed in the United Kingdom by Latimer Trend and Company Ltd, Plymouth.

ISBN 978 0 7492 1638 2

1.1

Contents

DU311 course team

Claire Appleby, Consultant

Dr Claudia Aradau, Course Team Member

Prof. Susan Baker, External Assessor

Sheree Barboteau, Course Specialist

Melanie Bayley, Media Project Manager

John Berriman, Service Delivery Team (VLE)

Prof. Andrew Blowers, Course Team Member

Dr Susan Board, Critical Reader (Block 1)

Dr William Brown, Deputy Course Team Chair and Block 2 Leader

Dr Jessica Budds, Course Team Member

Dr Nigel Clark, Consultant

Lene Connolly, Print Buyer

Dr Graham Dawson, Course Team Member

Fiona Durham, Learning and Teaching Librarian

Jane Fairclough, Critical Reader (Block 3)

Dr Juliet Fall, Course Team Member

Dr Susan Fawssett, Critical Reader (Block 2)

Alice Gallagher, Media Developer (Editor)

Bram Gieben, Course Team Member

Richard Golden, Production and Presentation Administrator

Dr Michael K. Goodman, External Author, King's College, London

Louise Hawker, Course Manager

Paul Hillery, Media Developer (Graphic Designer)

Owen Horn, Media Developer (S&V)

Dr David Humphreys, Block 1 Leader

Dr Petr Jehlička, Course Team Chair

Dr Pat Jess, Course Team Member

Shereen Karmali, Editor (freelance)

Jo Mack, Sound & Vision Producer

Dr Wendy Maples, Course Team Member

Dr Emma Mawdsley, External Author, Cambridge University

Andrew McDermott, Media Assistant

Isobel McLean, Indexer (freelance)

Margaret McManus, Media Assistant (Picture Research and Rights)

Katie Meade, Rights Executive

Joanne Osborn, Proofreader (freelance)

Dr Piya Pangsapa, External Author, State University of New York

Jason Platts, Media Developer (Interactive Media)

Eileen Potterton, Course Manager

Marilyn Reed, Media Production Co-ordinator

Dr Philip Sarre, Block 3 Leader

Dr Sandrine Simon, Course Team Member

Lynne Slocombe, Editor (freelance)

Dr Mark J. Smith, Course Team Member

Nikki Smith, Assistant Print Buyer

Prof. Robert Spicer, Consultant

Matt Staples, Consultant

Sam Thomas, Learning and Teaching Librarian

Prof. Grahame Thompson, Course Team Member

Howie Twiner, Media Developer (Graphic Artist)

Prof. Reece Walters, Course Team Member

Jo Woodward, Course Manager

Chris Wooldridge, Editor (freelance)

Introduction

Philip Sarre and Petr Jehlička

This course started from the assumption that the Earth faces a threefold environmental crisis. First, human society is impoverishing and disrupting the resources it uses to support itself, threatening both ecological and social sustainability. Second, national and international policy responses have been inadequate to overcome the problems, even to prevent them from becoming worse. Third, current understandings of climate change suggest that society has quite a short time window in which to respond before the crisis becomes self-perpetuating. After writing the course, that assessment now looks like an understatement.

The first two books of the course combine to show that the scale and complexity of the crisis is even greater than initially assumed. The problem of climate change, formidable in itself, connects to problems of biodiversity conservation, agriculture, water availability, urban problems and industrial pollution. Worse, the central cause of the complex of problems is the very process that has made human society more numerous and more prosperous than ever before – a form of development, based on industrialisation and competitive market exchange, that has proved to be very uneven within and between countries. Inadequate policy responses result from vested interests in further development of the same sort, compounded by the difficulties of responding to international, even global, problems through a state-dominated international political system. The time window, worsened by years of denial about climate change, is further shortened by the fact that for many hundreds of millions, crisis is already a way of life.

Yet, as well as this pessimistic assessment, Books 1 and 2 also offer some grounds for cautious optimism. Thanks to scientific, technological and social research, the nature and causes of most problems are better understood than they were; there is a range of alternative technologies available or in development; and there is increasing realisation that action needs to be taken to tackle the problems. There are also signs of positive policy response: the environmental movement has put many environmental issues on to national and international agendas; the United Nations (UN) has had some successes, perhaps most notably the Brundtland Report and the widespread recognition of sustainable development (SD) as an objective; some countries, and the European Union (EU) as a whole, have been leaders in policy development and implementation; there have been some successes in developing international environmental law and international environmental agreements; and some corporations have adopted policies for corporate social responsibility. Finally, the financial crisis starting in 2008 has provided an opportunity to reform the assumptions that have shaped development and governance since the 1970s.

Governance is an important concept for this book. It is used in several chapters to approach the issue of social change. Governance, you may recall, is a broader concept than government. Government denotes the formal collection of institutions in a political system – the state and its administrative agencies – that can enforce rules over a given territory. Governance, on the other hand, does not focus solely on the state but on all social structures and processes where collective goals are set. It is a contested concept, with different analysts providing different definitions. To the Commission on Global Governance, **global governance** includes not only intergovernmental relationships, such as international institutions. It also includes a range of public and private actors, including 'non-governmental organizations, citizens' movements, multinational corporations and the global capital markets' (Commission on Global Governance, 1995, pp. 2–3). The term 'governance' conveys the sense that politics and human affairs are managed through arrangements and rules negotiated by a plurality of actors. This notion suggests that environmental problems cannot be solved solely by governments or by international environmental institutions. The involvement of a range of other actors is also necessary, including individual citizens.

Global governance is the ordering of international politics and policy by a plurality of actors, including governments, international institutions, non-governmental organisations (NGOs), citizens' movements, business and the capital markets.

Outline of chapters

In considering the scope and opportunities for change in a diversity of settings, this book builds on insights from the previous two books. To that end, the authors start their chapters by looking at how the actors focused on in this book were introduced in Books 1 and 2. The chapters then expand on these insights further to develop a particular perspective which puts *course question 4* 'What can be done for the future, and what should be done?' at the centre of analysis. Thus, in accordance with this question, the book considers what changes might be desirable (raising questions of value) and what might be feasible politically. Rather than outlining utopian visions, we have chosen to focus on, and evaluate, examples of change which are currently happening, or being campaigned for – in other words, cases where individuals, groups or institutions are seeking to take responsibility for change. As indicated by the chapter titles, in the first four chapters we look for change in a number of different 'directions': 'up', meaning the organisations which have been given formal responsibilities for international governance; 'down', meaning grassroots organisations which have reacted to problems they care about, with significant effects; 'North', meaning within the developed world; and 'South', meaning within the developing world. All chapters in this book seek to avoid the temptation to attempt exhaustive coverage. Instead, they select examples that generate ideas and practices of wider, and potentially global, significance. In considering innovative practices, ideas and policies, several chapters engage with two further insights. The first insight is the extent to which policy and know-how transfers (North–South; West–East), often assumed to be an uncomplicated linear process, are in practice subject to interactions between the originator and recipient and to modifications arising from the cultural and political contexts. The second insight reverses the commonly held perspective that studies processes of policy transfer from developed to developing societies in terms of the latter's capacity to adopt imported innovations, and raises the question of circumstances under which minority or indigenous innovative practices can be adopted more widely and in other contexts.

This book starts from the position established by its precursors: if human society is to become sustainable, global governance will need to change significantly. Chapter 1 by David Humphreys, Piya Pangsapa and Mark J. Smith considers the most obvious actors involved in international governance – the UN and its agencies on the one hand and the international financial and trade organisations on the other. The UN has a good record of leadership in bringing environmental issues to the attention of the international community, from the 1972 Stockholm Conference onwards, and has attempted to reconcile environmental and development issues, notably in its sponsorship of the World Commission on Environment and Development (WCED). Its agencies, especially the United Nations Environment Programme (UNEP), play valuable roles in monitoring and problematising events. Yet, its successes are limited and its relations with the USA difficult. In contrast, the Bretton Woods institutions have been politically effective, perhaps because of their closeness to the USA, if less effective in promoting development and financial stability. The World Trade Organization (WTO) is different again, with strong enforcement powers, but seemingly unable to progress its development of free markets. The chapter asks whether these international governance arrangements could be reformed and integrated to give environmental and development issues and institutions greater priority.

In Chapter 2 Piya Pangsapa and Mark J. Smith look to the environmental movement, which transcended its apparently weak position to put environmental issues on to political agendas, and continues to generate new demands and insights. However, the initial movement has been largely incorporated into international governance and lost much of its radicalism. The leading edge now comes from a newer direction: the environmental justice movement (EJM), initially in the USA and then in other countries, has mobilised some of the most marginal communities to make demands for justice, in relation initially to exposure to toxic pollution. It has been remarkably effective. However, theoretical investigation of the EJM and of earlier 'new social movements' suggests that it is not just group identity, the strength of their grievances, their ability to mobilise resources or the extent of their international networking which influences their effectiveness, but also the structure of political opportunities within which they work. So the EJM has its main successes in democratic countries with constitutions that guarantee citizens rights: it points to desirable changes, but has made least progress in places where they are most needed. The chapter asks whether the EJM could be extended to newly industrialising countries.

In Chapter 3 Sandrine Simon looks to the places with maximum exposure to environmental and development problems and, seemingly, the weakest powers to address them. Surprisingly, the poorest citizens of the least developed countries contribute to several potentially radical ways forward. For years it was thought that these areas were concerned with development rather than environment, but more recently it has been realised that this obscured a basic feature of grassroots protests there: since livelihoods were based on environmental resources, protests about livelihood were also environmental. Because these countries are integrated with the world economy mainly as suppliers of resources and/or the products of cheap labour, such protests often confront the interests of poor people with those of domestic or foreign big business. Analysis of these kinds of disputes contributes to the development of 'political ecology', an approach which links ecological change to international political economy and hence implies that the solution of ecological problems requires the transformation of the international political economy. A step towards this is the attempt of governments in the South to use 'green accounting' to integrate their consideration of development opportunities, resource depletion and environmental degradation. In turn, this directs your attention to ecological economics, an approach which seeks to analyse economies as being embedded within ecosystems rather than independent from them. The chapter asks whether it would be desirable to use ecological economics rather than neoclassical economics as the basis of accounting and economic calculation.

Chapter 4 by Petr Jehlička focuses on the EU, which has emerged as the leader in international environmental negotiations and an advocate of sustainable development (SD), including sustainable consumption (SC). The chapter explains how the EU came to treat environment so centrally although the founding treaty focused on development of a single market. Using the example of policies for SC, it also evaluates the content of policy and concludes that the EU itself practises ecological modernisation even while it espouses SD. Even a powerful multinational organisation faces political and economic pressures to adopt neoliberal norms. Once more, this case study shows some promise, but less impressive delivery. From an environmentalist viewpoint, it would be desirable for the EU to practise what it preaches, but it is clear that it does not find it feasible to do so in today's competitive world.

The first four chapters of this book show that, in the present system of international governance, each component is constrained by the others. International economic and environmental governance organisations have limited scope for change because of pressures put on them by powerful states. Powerful states, even the second biggest economic bloc in the world, can't change unilaterally because international organisations, businesses and citizens insist on them being 'internationally competitive', and hence pursuing economic growth and profit. The environmental movement is opposed in the pursuit of environmental justice by both different diagnoses of what should be done and by the constraints of national and international politics. Although they are pursuing initiatives of their own, citizens, groups and governments in the South are bound into international power structures that inhibit policy responses. This mutual reinforcement is both a problem and an opportunity, in that each component constrains the others, but could also open up the possibility that change could become self-reinforcing, as changes in one component open up new possibilities for change in others, if only a way could be found to start the process. Consequently, the last chapter of the course asks what ethical arguments might influence citizens to take responsibility for change.

Earlier parts of the course have suggested that environmental politics pursues different values from those of mainstream international governance. Livelihood, ecosystem integrity, justice, quality of life, intra- and intergenerational equity are proposed as at least as worthy of consideration as economic growth or profit maximisation. In addition, whether citizens espouse neoliberalism or advocate participatory democracy, they are now expected to take responsibility and participate in governance. But how can you, as a student and citizen, make sense of the range of values on offer? In Chapter 5 Mark J. Smith uses some ideas from philosophical ethics – the academic discipline which explores concepts like 'right conduct' or 'the good life' – to try to make sense of, and to balance, the variety of values being advocated. The chapter explores some approaches to establishing ethical standards and their application in practice as part of citizenship, and suggests that it is down to each citizen to make ethical choices, in the light of their own conception of the good life.

In their quest to identify new approaches to resolving environmental and resource problems, the authors of these chapters consider how different actors, ranging from global institutions to individual citizens and consumers, can bring about change. In the chapters that follow, you will see, on a number of occasions, how these actors grapple with what is politically feasible and what is desirable and how the most desirable approaches or strategies are often subverted by political pragmatism and/or their lack of conceptual compatibility with the dominant ideology. However frustrating this may sometimes be, it can be argued, as indeed some of these chapters do, that what seems a compromise, a mainstream 'feasible' solution, may well turn out to be the first step towards a more fundamental and desirable change. What this book as a whole also shows, we would suggest, is that without attempts to think the unthinkable, without pushing for idealistic and desirable goals, even those solutions that are ultimately regarded as merely reformist or 'feasible', would often fail to materialise.

Reference

Commission on Global Governance (1995) *Our Global Neighbourhood: The Report of the Commission on Global Governance*, Oxford, Oxford University Press.

Chapter 1
Look up: reforming international governance

David Humphreys, Piya Pangsapa and Mark J. Smith

Contents

1 Introduction

Throughout this course some important debates have emerged. In this chapter we wish to pursue two distinct, but interlinked, debates. First, can we reconcile environmental protection and sustainability with development and free trade (*course theme 4*)? Second, can existing intergovernmental institutions effectively address global environmental problems, or do they need reform, or maybe even replacing? In this chapter these two debates are addressed in the spirit of *course question 4*, 'What can be done for the future, and what should be done?' This question requires an examination of the desirability and feasibility of different proposals for change.

As you saw in the Introduction to this book, we start with the assumption that in order to overcome global environmental problems there will need to be some change in global governance in the broadest sense. So an obvious starting point is to consider the international institutions, set up by treaties between states, that currently influence environmental problems and policy. As explained in Book 2, these include not only organisations with an environmental remit, such as the United Nations Environment Programme (UNEP), but also organisations with economic and development concerns. Within the broad range of international organisations that exert some influence over the environment, we pay attention to two sets: UN bodies with an environmental focus; and organisations with an economic and development mandate, namely the World Bank and the International Monetary Fund (IMF) (collectively known as the Bretton Woods Institutions, or BWIs) and the World Trade Organization (WTO).

This division between these two sets of international organisations is not just a question of administrative structures; it also embodies a clash of values. In his book *People Before Profit* (2002), sociologist Charles Derber argues that we are living through an ideological battle between two constitutional traditions. In the first tradition human rights and social welfare are central. To Derber this tradition is based on the principles of the US Bill of Rights, the 1948 Universal Declaration of Human Rights and European social democracy. The second tradition is a business-based constitutionalism expressed through the IMF, World Bank and, in particular, the WTO, in which corporate rights and capitalist expansion dominate. Reforming the organisations will entail rebalancing these traditions.

We begin (Section 2) by surveying the constraints to more effective environmental policies (*course question 3*) that were examined in Book 2. We then examine the roles the UN has played in responding to international environmental problems (Section 3) before broadening our analysis of global governance to consider the role that international economic and financial institutions may play in tackling environmental and developmental problems (Section 4). Next we introduce some proposals to create a World Environment Organisation (WEO), considering how such an organisation may contribute to a more sustainable model of global governance (Section 5). We then briefly examine the history of international negotiations between the developed and less developed countries, using forests as a case study (Section 6).

For much of this chapter we take a narrow look at global governance, examining the role of international institutions. However, we do not lose sight of the role of other actors, such as local authorities, business, non-governmental organisations (NGOs) and awareness-raising events, such as the concert illustrated in Figure 1.1. The organiser of Live Earth, Al Gore, argued that tackling climate change requires individual citizens to reduce greenhouse gas emissions as well as action by the world's

Figure 1.1
The Australian musician and environmental campaigner Rob Hirst performs with his band Ghostwriters at the Live Earth concert in Sydney on 7 July 2007 (07-07-07)

governments and businesses. Towards the end of the chapter we suggest that reform of international institutions first requires change at other levels of global governance, especially within the state (Section 7).

1.1 Learning outcomes

This chapter should enable you to:

- discuss different perspectives on global governance reform in terms of competing values
- assess the arguments for and against reform of UNEP, including proposals to create a WEO
- critically assess the existing and potential role of international financial and economic institutions in global governance
- critically evaluate the relationship between the state and global governance.

2 What sort of reform?

We start this chapter with a presumption that some reform of global governance is desirable from an environmental standpoint. While there have been various attempts to introduce environmental policies into global governance, such attempts have, so far, had limited success. This is not to say that the environmental policies that have been introduced to date are 'wrong' and that there is no place for them in a reformed global governance. It would, for example, be misguided to dismiss policy responses such as multinational carbon emissions trading systems and business self-regulation if they genuinely contribute to more sustainable models of governance. Our case, rather, is that such policies are not proving to be effective fast enough.

Carbon emissions trading systems were introduced in Book 1, Chapter 3 and business self-regulation was discussed in Book 2, Chapter 10

2.1 Identifying the constraints

In some respects problems such as environmental degradation are similar to medical problems: the cure that is prescribed will depend on how the problem is diagnosed. What this suggests is that before we can approach the question 'What can be done for the future, and what should be done?' (*course question 4*) we first need to review some of the main constraints to more effective environmental policy responses (*course question 3*).

Activity 1.1

Summarise what you consider to be the main constraints to more effective environmental policies that you learnt about in Book 2. You may like to concentrate only on certain chapters, such as those by Emma Mawdsley, William Brown, Reece Walters and Philip Sarre (Chapters 2, 7, 8 and 9).

Gross domestic product is defined as the total market value of all goods and services produced within a country in the calendar year.

Emma Mawdsley argues that some development strategies produce more adverse environmental impacts than others. All types of society – capitalist, mixed economies, state socialism – have invested resources in economic growth as their primary objective, with **gross domestic product** (GDP) – defined as the total market value of all goods and services produced within a country in the calendar year – usually adopted as the measure of 'success'. This does not, however, mean that all forms of development are damaging; some development strategies may be more sustainable than others. What seems to matter is whether environmental and social objectives have been pursued as integral features of development; in most countries they have not.

William Brown argues that agreeing effective environmental policies through intergovernmental negotiations is difficult when governments seek to promote the collective interest while simultaneously seeking to realise their own self-interests. State sovereignty acts as a constraint on more effective forms of global environmental governance. The responsiveness of national governments is shaped by a variety of factors, with key variables including the costs of tackling environmental problems (especially if these are significant in the short term) and different perceptions of ecological vulnerability. Much also depends on whether states agree on the causes of an environmental problem, the measures needed to address it, and whether the problem warrants an urgent response. The case of atmospheric ozone depletion rated 'high' on all three counts, which led to prompt agreement to cut chlorofluorocarbons (CFCs); but where this is not the case international agreement can be harder to obtain. William Brown points out that in practice agreement has been easier for more focused issues and that states often opt for weak measures in the hope of a high degree of acceptance.

Reece Walters focuses on legal constraints to more effective environmental policy. He argues that conventional approaches to environmental law currently make it difficult to prohibit certain types of action that degrade the environment. He suggests that in a world shaped by different legal systems and ways of understanding the environment, a new notion of *environmental crime* may overcome current legal constraints on policy making that undermine the willingness of political institutions to act. Reece Walters argues that the criminalisation of negative environmental externalities in national and international environmental law has the potential to transform obligations into duties that will be legally enforced. However, to be successful, this first needs political will. The concept of **political will** is an elusive one but it may be broadly defined as the determination and commitment of a political system to implement a desired policy, irrespective of the costs and constraints.

On the concept of negative externalities see Book 1, Chapter 3

Political will refers to the determination and commitment of a political system to implement a desired policy, irrespective of the costs and constraints.

Philip Sarre's central argument is that governance is dominated not by environmental concerns but by economic ones. Economic governance both systemically impacts upon the environment and constrains the construction of more effective environmental policies. He explores some of the effects of neoliberalism on global environmental issues, for example through the practices of the BWIs, the World Bank and the IMF. For Sarre, the current neoliberal economic order emphasises profit making, encourages tax avoidance by corporations, leads to the widespread externalisation of environmental costs and erodes labour and health standards.

Taken together, these chapters suggest there is a considerable degree of inconsistency in different international agreements. Governments agree, or fail to agree, different treaties at different times, focusing on discrete issues but neglecting the interactions between them.

2.2 Problem-solving and critical approaches

Solving environmental problems clearly cannot be achieved by focusing on environmental policy alone. Some consideration of economic governance more generally is essential. An important question that then arises is: do we need to change the broader structures and processes of global governance in order to solve environmental problems and, if so, how radical must change be?

There is no clear-cut answer to this question. Different actors will give different responses according to their political values and their knowledge of environmental problems (*course theme 3*). Analytically, however, we may distinguish between two types of response, between problem-solving and critical approaches, as argued by the political theorist Robert Cox (1986) and applied to international environmental problems by Lorraine Elliott (2004).

A **problem-solving approach** seeks to solve an environmental problem without questioning the foundational principles, values and power relations of social order. Existing social structures, institutions and political interests are accepted. The status quo thus establishes the parameters within which change can take place. Problem-solving approaches are essentially reformist; they advocate *system adaptation* to

A **problem-solving approach** seeks to solve environmental problems without questioning the foundational principles, values and power relations of social order.

problems, but no more than this. A problem-solving approach would look to the state and international institutions to take the lead in solving environmental problems.

A **critical approach** allows for system transformation by admitting the possibility that contemporary social structures, institutions and power distributions could themselves contribute to the problem.

A **critical approach** to environmental problems would not assume a priori that a problem could be solved within existing structures and institutions. A critical approach challenges existing ways of thinking, seeking innovative solutions. It does not accept that there should be limits to social change, and is prepared to admit the possibility that contemporary social structures, institutions and power distributions could themselves constitute part of the problem; in which case a problem-solving approach might leave the underlying causes of the problem unchallenged. While a problem-solving approach seeks system adaptation, a critical approach would argue for *system transformation*. The difference between the two is not simply a quantitative question of the degree of change; it is a qualitative question of the type of change. Critical approaches do not accept things as they are, but allow for the possibility of a very different world. So a critical approach is, if necessary, prepared to call into question those things that a problem-solving approach would not, such as the role of the state and the international state system in environmental degradation and dominant ideological beliefs, such as neoliberalism.

The distinction between the two types of approaches is very much an ideal type, but it is a useful distinction for thinking through the constraints on more effective policies (*course question 3*). Some constraints can be addressed and overcome fairly easily within existing social structures and without challenging dominant interests and power relationships. Such constraints can be overcome with a problem-solving approach. However, where constraints cannot be easily overcome, with the result that environmental policies persistently fail to solve the problem under consideration, then a more critical approach may be needed. The most persistent environmental problems may require deep social change.

The distinction between the two approaches is also useful when considering *course question 4*. You will recall from Book 1, Chapter 1 that the first part of this question – What can be done? – requires an awareness of the feasibility of a particular policy proposal. The second part of this question – What should be done? – requires an examination of ethics. In theory those environmental policy proposals that are likely to be the most feasible, in the sense that they are favoured within existing policy-making structures, are those that do not challenge dominant political interests; in other words, a problem-solving approach. But a policy that is feasible in political terms, and which attracts widespread political support, may not necessarily be effective in environmental terms. Similarly, a critical approach that challenges established and powerful actors is less likely to be politically feasible,

The idea of effectiveness was introduced in Book 1, Chapter 1 even if it holds out the promise of more effective solutions and is thus desirable in ethical terms.

As argued above, reversing environmental degradation is likely to require some reforms to global governance. However, whether these changes will be relatively small scale and at the problem-solving end of the spectrum, or fundamental, radical and sufficiently far reaching as to constitute a critical approach, is a matter of intense political debate. The distinction between the two types of approaches is an analytical one rather than one that is drawn by policy makers. Analytically, most existing environmental policy responses fit into the realm of problem solving, although this does not, of course, mean that they should necessarily be dismissed because of that. Critical approaches are conceptual and theoretical. They are rarely advocated by mainstream policy makers. Nonetheless, some of the solutions favoured by environmental activists and green parties should be seen as critical approaches (see Section 7 below). Critical approaches are not immediately possible and can only be achieved, if at all, after long-term resistance and social mobilisation.

In the remainder of this chapter we provide a flavour of some of the different international governance reform proposals that have been advocated, and of the different ethical standpoints that underlie these proposals. We start by examining the responses to environmental problems that have been developed within the UN.

3 The United Nations

In 1945 the powers that emerged victorious from World War II created a new multilateral international system, the UN. The term **multilateralism** refers to multiple governments cooperating to solve shared problems. (In distinction, unilateralism is action by one state acting alone, while bilateralism refers to decisions agreed by two states.) At the time of its creation the objective of the UN was to promote international stability through the prevention and peaceful resolution of conflicts through diplomacy. At Bretton Woods, the World Bank and IMF were established to promote economic recovery and financial stability. The UN was strongly influenced by the human rights tradition, but it had no mandate to deal with environmental issues. Indeed, neither the UN Charter which created the UN in 1945 nor the Universal Declaration of Human Rights adopted by the United Nations General Assembly in 1948 even mention the word 'environment'. However, the Universal Declaration of Human Rights does state that 'Everyone has the right to life, liberty and security of person' (UN, 1948, Article 3), a right that is consistent with the maintenance of a sustainable planet.

Multilateralism refers to multiple governments cooperating together to solve shared problems.

The role of the Security Council in climate change was examined in Book 1, Chapter 5

The UN is a collection of intergovernmental organisations and agencies rather than a single organisation or an integrated and coherent system. The two most important UN institutions are the Security Council, with five permanent members (China, France, Russia, the UK and the USA) and ten non-permanent members, and the General Assembly, open to all UN member states and which operates on a one-state-one-vote basis. The Economic and Social Council (ECOSOC) has responsibility for the UN's work on economic and social affairs. It reports directly to the General Assembly and has a membership of 54 states, with equal representation among the world's regions. Under Article 71 of the UN Charter, the ECOSOC may consult with NGOs 'which are concerned with matters within its competence' (UN, 1945, Article 71). The ECOSOC has gradually taken on responsibility for environmental issues.

Most multilateral environmental agreements owe their origins to the UN. The negotiations for the Framework Convention on Climate Change (FCCC) were established by the General Assembly (Book 1, Chapters 1 and 4). UNEP has organised negotiations for the Convention on Biological Diversity (Book 2, Chapter 5), the Vienna Convention for the Protection of the Ozone Layer and the Basel Convention on Control of Transboundary Movements of Hazardous Wastes and Their Disposal (Book 2, Chapter 7).

Activity 1.2

In Books 1 and 2 you encountered several examples where the UN undertook initiatives to manage international environmental problems. Make a note of as many of these initiatives as you can. They include international conferences, UN-sponsored multilateral environmental agreements, and institutions created by the UN to handle environmental issues.

So far three major UN environmental conferences have been held, as discussed in Book 2, Chapters 7, 8 and 9. The first two led to the creation of new UN environment institutions.

3.1 United Nations Conference on the Human Environment, Stockholm 1972

The 1972 UNCHE was discussed in Book 2, Chapters 7, 8 and 9

An example of UNEP's catalytic initiative – on sustainable consumption (SC) – is introduced in Chapter 4 of this book

You learnt in Book 2, Chapter 7 that the United Nations Conference on the Human Environment (UNCHE) in Stockholm in 1972 agreed to create a United Nations environment programme. Based in Nairobi, UNEP has two mandates: catalytic and coordination (Figure 1.2). UNEP acts to *catalyse* environmental policy in the UN system by calling upon established UN organs to deal with environmental issues (rather than attempt to handle such issues itself). As part of its catalytic mandate

Figure 1.2
'Green City in the Sun' Nairobi, one of Africa's most populous cities with an estimated population of more than 3 million, has been home to the UNEP since 1973

UNEP has hosted negotiations for many multilateral environmental agreements. UNEP's *coordination* mandate is to coordinate environmental activities in the UN system. It has become clear as environmental problems have worsened that UNEP, with a staff of just a few hundred, simply does not have the capacity to meet these two vast challenges. Mark Imber (1993) has argued that UNEP has proved successful with its catalytic mandate, both internationally and in pioneering small-scale environmental programmes within countries, but coordination of environmental work within the UN has proved to be an 'unfair burden'.

3.2 United Nations Conference on Environment and Development, Rio de Janeiro 1992

In 1991, in the run-up to the 1992 United Nations Conference on Environment and Development (UNCED, popularly known as the 'Earth Summit'), UNEP together with the United Nations Development Programme (UNDP) and the World Bank helped to establish the Global Environment Facility (GEF), which funds environmental projects that will yield global benefits (Box 1.1 and Figure 1.3). Although the GEF has never been funded at a level commensurate with its responsibilities, in principle it is a role model for international governance, since its 'governance structure is a unique example of how different traditions of UN and Bretton Woods agencies can be brought together' (Streck, 2001, p. 90).

Box 1.1 Global Environment Facility

The GEF was created in 1991 and endorsed at the 1992 UNCED. Its implementing agencies are the World Bank, UNDP and UNEP. The chair resides in the World Bank's Environment Department. The GEF is intended to mobilise new and additional financial resources to fund the incremental costs necessary to implement policies that yield global environmental benefits. These policies must be consistent with multilateral environmental agreements recognised by the GEF, namely:

- Framework Convention on Climate Change, 1992, and the Kyoto Protocol
- Convention on Biological Diversity, 1992
- Regional and international waters agreements
- Vienna Convention for the Protection of the Ozone Layer, 1985, and the Montreal Protocol
- Convention to Combat Desertification, 1994
- Stockholm Convention on Persistent Organic Pollutants, 2001.

Figure 1.3
Map of the Black Sea. The GEF has funded a water quality protection project in the Black Sea

The UNCED indicated that international support for action on the environment was widespread but limited. As described in Book 2, Chapter 9, the conference did not adopt the Earth Charter and opted for a weakened interpretation of sustainable development (SD). A proposal for a WEO was watered down and led to the creation of a much more limited institution. The Commission on Sustainable Development (CSD) meets annually in New York and reports to the ECOSOC. It is charged with overseeing national measures to implement Agenda 21, an ambitious programme of action for SD adopted at the UNCED. However, Agenda 21, like the Rio Declaration on Environment and Development also agreed in 1992, is a non-legally binding document and national implementation is discretionary. Unlike 'hard' multilateral environmental agreements, Agenda 21 is not ratified through domestic legislatures. It comprises 'soft' political objectives rather than legal commitments. Two 'hard' legal instruments were agreed at Rio – on climate change and biodiversity – but a planned forests convention was not agreed (Section 6.2 below).

The 1992 UNCED was discussed in Book 2, Chapters 7, 8 and 9

The process of ratification was introduced in Book 1, Chapter 4

The UNCED process also led to an expansion in the number of NGOs granted consultation status at the ECOSOC. Any NGO granted consultation status at the ECOSOC is now automatically granted consultative status at the CSD (Willetts, 1996). The CSD also holds regular 'multistakeholder dialogues', informal discussions at which representatives from business, indigenous communities, trade unionists, scientists and environmental groups and other stakeholders may make statements and exchange views. However, during the formal negotiations decision making remains the exclusive prerogative of states. NGOs may attend these negotiations as observers, not as participants. Here it is worth drawing a distinction between **consultation** and **participation**. A consultative arrangement is an understanding that actors may be asked to provide their views on an issue to policy makers. A participative arrangement involves a genuine opportunity to partake in policy making and to affect outcomes. While there is a growing recognition within the UN that NGOs and other stakeholders should be consulted, genuine participation of NGOs remains a concession, rather than a right.

Consultation is an arrangement whereby actors may be asked to provide their views on an issue to policy makers. **Participation** is an arrangement whereby actors have a genuine opportunity to partake in policy making and to affect outcomes.

The involvement of actors other than government is also being encouraged at the local level, although whether the arrangements are consultative or participative varies enormously from place to place. Local authorities are encouraged to implement Local Agenda 21 (LA21) programmes. Some LA21 programmes have replicated traditional top-down management, with minimal participation from stakeholders

The concept of deliberative democracy was introduced in Book 1, Chapter 6

(Lafferty and Eckerberg, 1998). Others have mobilised a range of groups, encouraging the development of new forms of governance where the state engages with stakeholders in local deliberative decision-making processes. According to Gerard Mullally (1998) the most successful LA21 initiatives are those that avoid traditional public meetings with a preset agenda and instead have innovative forms of participation such as consensus conferencing, focus groups, citizens' juries and direct involvement from affected constituencies with a voice in the decision-making process. Implementation of LA21 programmes has been enormously varied over time and between different places (*course theme 5*). The case of LA21 illustrates that there is a connection between global governance and the local level. Policies agreed at the international level will have no impact unless they are translated into local level action.

3.3 World Summit on Sustainable Development, Johannesburg 2002

The 2002 WSSD was discussed in Book 2, Chapter 9

The third UN summit on the environment was the 2002 United Nations World Summit on Sustainable Development (WSSD) held in Johannesburg. It granted widespread consultative rights to NGOs and major groups (Figure 1.4). The summit attempted to maintain the momentum of LA21 action plans launched at Rio, but with a renewed focus on making cities and communities more sustainable. It linked environmental sustainability to other UN objectives such as the Millennium Development Goals. The summit recognised that half the world's population live in urban environments and that ways should be found to reduce the ecological footprint of cities through sustainable municipal management. Explicit in the Johannesburg Plan of Action that the summit adopted is the recognition that urban living can have considerable impacts on water and air quality, climate, soil, food production, biodiversity and human health. The summit recognised that social and environmental injustices need to be tackled together rather than in isolation. However, while the conference was strong on rhetoric and soft agreements, environmentalists were disappointed by the lack of hard agreements.

For a summary of the Millennium Development Goals see Book 2, Chapter 9, Box 9.1

On the concept of ecological footprint see Book 1, Chapter 1 and Book 2, Chapter 1

3.4 The United Nations and corporate regulation

One area of UN policy making where there has been long-standing debate concerns the regulation of transnational corporations. Prior to the 1992 UNCED, there were plans for states to finalise the negotiation of a code of conduct to regulate transnational corporations. However, agreement proved to be impossible to reach. Major business corporations

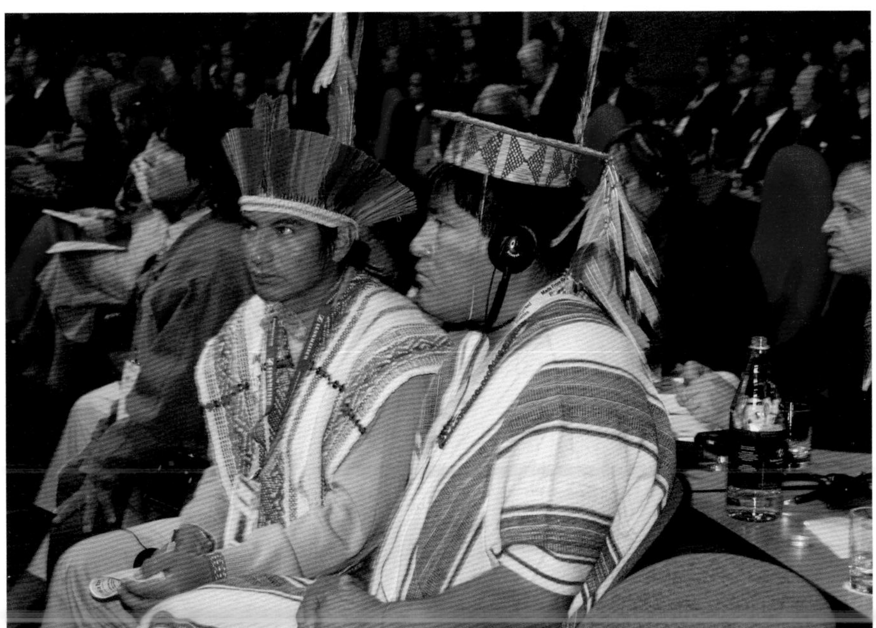

Figure 1.4
The WSSD was held in Johannesburg, South Africa in 2002

Figure 1.4a
Indigenous peoples' representatives, granted consultative status, confer during the summit

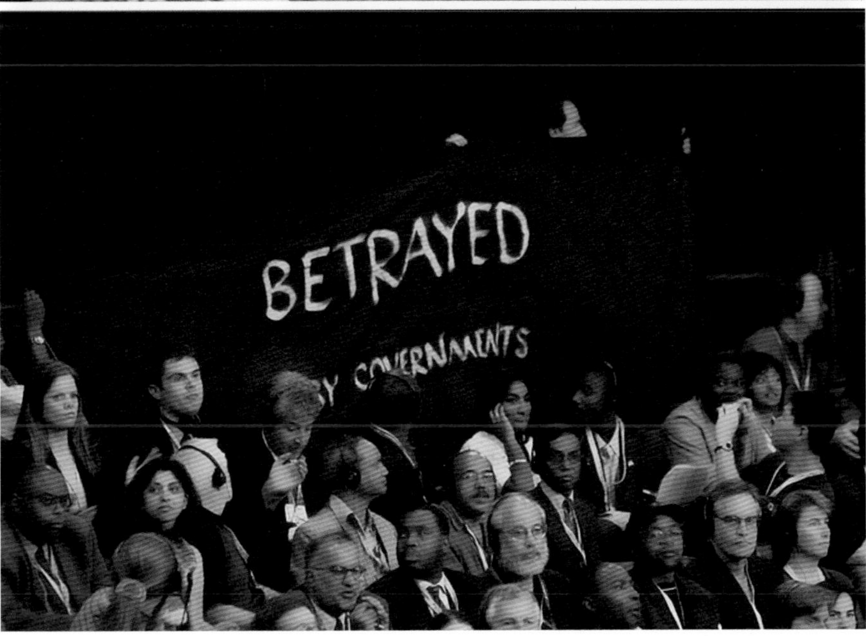

Figure 1.4b
A critical approach? Political demonstrations by those granted consultative status at UN conferences are very rare. This protest at Johannesburg was an exception. The banner reads 'Betrayed by governments'

lobbied strongly against a code, which can be seen as contrary to the free market ethos of neoliberalism. Several developed country governments opposed the idea. Nevertheless, the defeat of the proposal for a UN code of conduct has not led to a closure of the debate on global corporate regulation, although it has shifted the political space within which the debate is played out. One of the arguments made by business is that business itself should agree the ethical standards that guide it. However, little progress was made until 1999 when Kofi Annan, then the UN secretary general, engaged in a process of outreach to the business community. At the 1999 World Economic Forum at Davos, Switzerland, Annan addressed the chief executives of some of the world's largest business corporations:

> We have to choose between a global market driven only by calculations of short-term profit, and one which has a human face; between a world which condemns a quarter of the human race to starvation and squalor, and one which offers everyone at least a chance of prosperity, in a healthy environment, between a selfish free-for-all in which we ignore the fate of the losers, and a future in which the strong and successful accept their responsibilities, showing global vision and leadership.
>
> (Annan, 1999)

This speech prompted the adoption of the UN Global Compact, which was adopted in 2000, and included provisions on human rights, labour standards and environmental sustainability (Book 2, Chapter 10).

Activity 1.3

Can the UN Global Compact be considered a multilateral initiative? You might find it helpful to look again at the definition of multilateralism provided above and at the analysis of the Global Compact in Book 2, Chapter 10.

The UN secretary general used his authority and status to promote the Global Compact. Nonetheless, the initiative bypasses and, it may be argued, diminishes the role of intergovernmental bodies within the UN. It is not a multilateral initiative as no governments were involved in the agreement of the compact.

This raises the questions of who should set the rules in global governance, and in whose interests. Earlier in the course a distinction was drawn between the public and private sectors (Book 2, Chapter 5). A similar distinction applies in global governance. The public sector comprises states, or more accurately the governments that represent states, and intergovernmental organisations of which states are members. An intergovernmental organisation has the task of representing the interests of the global public in much the same way as a government is charged with representing the interests of its public. Of course, the public interest is an essentially contested concept; different actors may disagree on how the public interest should be articulated and realised. David Coleman (2003) has argued that by appealing directly to corporations to adopt global standards for business and, in so doing, inferring that states and intergovernmental organisations are laggards at standard setting, the Global Compact has subverted public decision making by passing business regulation to the private sector.

There are different views of corporate social responsibility (CSR) schemes such as the Global Compact. Critics argue that CSR schemes do not eliminate conflicts of interest between shareholder interests and environmental and social objectives. They claim that companies will always prioritise profit making and maximising shareholder value over all other responsibilities. Supporters of CSR argue that self-regulation and schemes such as the Global Compact are prompting a reconfiguration of governance that provides a baseline of standards for responsible corporate conduct. On this view, self-regulation can lead to standard raising in a not dissimilar way to regulation from governments and intergovernmental organisations.

Corporate social responsibility was introduced in Book 2, Chapter 10

3.5 The United Nations and the environment: a summary

The UN was set up to deal with peacekeeping, conflict resolution and economic and social concerns; environmental concerns have often been refracted through the lenses of these concerns. In the absence of a mandate to deal with environmental affairs, the UN's handling of international environmental problems has tended to emerge in an ad hoc and incremental manner. The organisation has no coherent environmental policy-making apparatus. Its coverage of environmental issues is uneven and disconnected. For some issues there is duplication of effort, while for others there are gaps. For example, there is no international convention on forests, and UN policy making on forests is fragmented across several UN organisations. There are also significant overlaps between UN environmental policy and UN bodies involved in social, cultural and economic policy frameworks. These organisational problems raise the question of whether the UN has the organisational capacity to address international environmental problems and, if not, what should be done to reform the organisation (*course question 4*).

We will consider some options for reforming the UN in Section 5 below. However, first we would like to invite you to examine another attribute of global governance that has major effects on environmental policy. It is a problem that Philip Sarre identified in Book 2, Chapter 9. Simply put, in global governance short-term economic concerns tend to prevail over long-term environmental ones.

4 Global economic governance

The desirability of reconciling the international governance of the economy, the environment and development has been a recurring theme over decades: it was noted at UNCED in 1992, at the WSSD in 2002, in formulating the Millennium Development Goals and restated in 2005 by the Group of 20 (G20), the expanded 'club' of the largest economies. Nevertheless, in practice the economy has been prioritised and international governance, particularly as expressed by the BWIs and the WTO, has focused on freeing international markets. Although calls for reform have been resisted in the past, two very different types of global problem are strengthening calls for major changes to global economic governance.

The first is environmental degradation, in particular the growing acceptance that climate change is happening and may have serious consequences. The second is the turmoil in international financial markets. In 2008 some major international banks went bankrupt while others were taken into partial or full state ownership following multibillion dollar rescue packages from the US government and governments in Europe. This crisis, the first in the post-war international economy to affect several developed countries simultaneously, has questioned the wisdom of freeing international capital markets. Both environmental degradation and financial instability have led to calls for tougher regulation of banks and business. However, new rules to address one problem will not necessarily address the other. For example, it is unlikely that regulating banks and business to ensure the stability of the international financial system will enhance environmental stability, and vice versa. An international regulatory framework that addresses both problems is increasingly seen to be not only desirable but also necessary.

Activity 1.4

Look back at Book 2, Chapter 9 and note some of the critiques of the BWIs and WTO, and the reforms suggested.

Our brief summary of pertinent points in Chapter 9 is as follows. While the World Bank is credited with improving environmental assessment of projects through the 1990s, it is also criticised for funding projects that have generated environmental degradation (Figure 1.5). The IMF is seen as unsuccessful in maintaining international stability or in assisting countries in difficulty. Both the World Bank and IMF are criticised for their adherence to the Washington Consensus when even IMF researchers had shown that open capital markets are neither necessary nor sufficient to promote development (Prasad et al., 2003). Furthermore, both have been criticised by environmentalists and those concerned with inequitable economic development for imposing neoliberal policies through structural adjustment programmes (SAPs). However the BWIs amended their aims to target poverty around the millennium. The WTO is criticised for prioritising trade rules over environmental protection, generating poverty and inequality and for favouring the interests of developed countries. Curiously, the WTO is criticised by many as excessively powerful, though it has been unable to progress its free trade agenda since 1995. Finally, in Book 2, Chapter 9 it was noted that critiques came both from sources in favour of more state intervention and from those in favour of even freer markets.

Structural adjustment programmes were introduced in Book 2, Chapter 2 and discussed in Book 2, Chapters 3, 4 and 9

Figure 1.5
In the mid 1980s the World Bank came under intense criticism for helping to fund the Grande Carajas project, an agricultural colonisation and mineral exploitation scheme in the Brazilian Amazon

Whereas some take a critical approach, arguing that the World Bank, IMF and WTO should be closed down and replaced by new agencies in the UN (Horten, 1995), others argue for reforms that are more modest but more feasible. In this brief section it is impossible to discuss all the proposals for reform to global economic governance so we will be selective.

4.1 Good governance at the Bretton Woods Institutions

The BWIs – the World Bank and IMF – are formally part of the UN, although they are, to all intents and purposes, independent bodies that determine their own policies. In both institutions decisions are made by quota voting, with the voting share of each member state being determined by its contribution, which depends on the size of its economy. This means that the wealthy donor states dominate policy making. By tradition the president of the World Bank is appointed by the USA while the managing director of the IMF is a European.

The IMF has no environmental policy. Its main task is to oversee the stability of the global financial system and provide short-term assistance to countries experiencing financial problems. In 2002 the IMF was heavily criticised by former World Bank chief economist and Nobel laureate Joseph Stiglitz for prescribing macroeconomic policies to many developing countries that left them vulnerable to currency speculators. Further, Stiglitz (2002, pp. 208–9) argued that the policies prescribed by the IMF often led to crises becoming deeper: indebted countries are granted rescue loans to pay off banks in developed countries which increases the long-term debt burden on indebted countries, leading to a debt spiral and impoverishment.

While the World Bank now has elaborate environmental safeguards over project lending, until recently the justification of its projects and the assumptions behind its other lending reflected the Washington Consensus assumptions also used by the IMF in SAPs: government controls and spending should be reduced, often by reducing education and health spending, markets should be opened and exports should be increased to earn hard currency to pay off debts. For many countries SAPs have led to the export of natural resources. Critics argue that these changes have damaged institutions, including governments, in less developed countries, increased poverty and exploited the environment (Book 2, Chapter 9). These criticisms have been rejected by the BWIs, but in the run-up to the millennium both made poverty reduction a priority (World Bank, 1998; IMF, 2008a). Both recognised that countries should ‘own’ their development policies, that low-income countries should be allowed to delay opening capital markets and that there might be more than one way to pursue development. Nonetheless, their own independent evaluation bodies have suggested that the changes in rhetoric have made little difference to their behaviour, and a recent evaluation of the World Bank suggested that its country-based structure weakened its ability to deal coherently with 'shared global challenges' like climate change and disease (IEG, 2008).

Like many aid organisations, the BWIs have recently put a great deal of stress on 'good governance' in dealing with their clients, so it seems reasonable to ask how their own governance processes match up to this ideal, which is pithily stated in the paragraph below.

> Good governance has 8 major characteristics. It is participatory, consensus oriented, accountable, transparent, responsive, effective and efficient, equitable and inclusive and follows the rule of law. It assures that corruption is minimized, the views of minorities are taken into account and that the voices of the most vulnerable in society are heard in decision making.
>
> (United Nations Economic and Social Commission for Asia and the Pacific, 2008)

The BWI systems of quota voting may be transparent, at least to those willing to unravel complex formulae, but they prioritise the views of the powerful rather than the vulnerable. They have taken some note of this criticism. For example, in 2008 the IMF Executive Board accepted a package of proposals intended to increase the votes of newly industrialising countries like South Korea and China (IMF, 2008b). However, critics complained that the change was marginal, and failed to recognise the true economic weight of these countries, let alone reflect the interests of the world's majority of poor people. Pressure for change in BWI governance will certainly persist, and will probably achieve at least gradual improvement.

4.2 The World Trade Organization: going critical?

In some respects, the WTO's decision-making processes are preferable to the BWIs. Policy decisions are taken on the basis of consensus, and in the event of a vote being needed, each member has one vote. Nonetheless, decisions are often taken by small groups of countries in informal, unannounced meetings that leave the majority disenfranchised. Even when debates take place among the full membership, and with appropriate preparations, powerful countries with more negotiators, more technical specialists and more scope for side payments tend to prevail, as with all international negotiations. However, the Doha round of negotiations has shown that less powerful countries who believe that their interests are not being properly reflected

Side payments were introduced in Book 1, Chapter 4

Disciplinary neoliberalism is a model of capitalism that operates through market forces and interventions of powerful states to support the rights of business and investors over other rights.

have the option of blocking change. Without a more fundamental reappraisal, the WTO risks being marginalised.

The WTO has been criticised for being too strong. Anti-globalisation campaigners, environmentalists and human rights activists complain that the WTO pursues the interests of the powerful – developed countries, transnational corporations (TNCs) and investors – at the expense of the environment and of human rights. The strength of the WTO in relation to environmental law forms part of what Stephen Gill (1995, 2002) has termed **disciplinary neoliberalism**, namely the ascendancy of the rights of businesses and investors over other rights, such as human rights or the right to a clean environment. Disciplinary neoliberalism is a model of capitalism that operates through a combination of market forces and the intervention of powerful states, in particular the G8 countries, to support the rights of business and investors. The WTO has a stronger normative force in shaping the behaviour of states and businesses than does international environmental law because it has tougher enforcement provisions. States have given the WTO the authority to require changes to national law consistent with WTO rules on pain of sanctions. Relatively few multilateral environmental agreements (the Montreal Protocol is one) have such strong provisions. The WTO also has procedures for resolving any trade disputes that may arise between WTO members. Robyn Eckersley (2004) has extended the concept of disciplinary neoliberalism when arguing that states have become increasingly self-censoring when negotiating multilateral environmental agreements, avoiding any measures that they think would be challenged at the WTO.

The WTO rejects this line of criticism, claiming that it has no power beyond what states are willing to give it (indeed its website suggests that it is no more than a table around which countries negotiate [WTO, 2007]). It claims it is mandated to deal with trade but in no way denies the right of countries to legislate on environmental or other standards, provided that they do not do so in ways that discriminate between countries. Its view is that free trade is consistent with SD. What is not at issue is that the WTO combines clear principles on trade and investment liberalisation, consolidated international agreements on detailed policies, and binding enforcement provisions in a way that makes it more effective than other international agencies.

However, its paralysis in policy development poses critical questions. Resistance from less developed countries, especially to agricultural subsidies in the USA and EU, has meant that the WTO has been unable to implement further trade liberalisation since its creation in 1995. Its own logic has exposed tensions between its concept of fair competition and the wide discrepancies in health, labour and environmental standards between rich and poor countries (Book 2, Chapter 9). In short, there are some unresolved contradictions between WTO's stated objectives, the means it adopts and the context in which it is working.

The preamble to the agreement establishing the WTO identifies its objectives including: 'raising standards of living' in developing countries, and especially the least developed countries, as well as developed ones; 'seeking both to protect and preserve the environment'; and hence 'sustainable development' (WTO, 1994). This updates the language of Article XX of the 1947 General Agreement on Trade and Tariffs (GATT), which gives countries the right to take measures 'necessary to protect human, animal or plant life or health' (paragraph XX(b)) or 'relating to the conservation of exhaustible natural resources' (paragraph XX(g)) (WTO, undated). The Doha Declaration further emphasises both developmental and environmental objectives, and suggests that they are mutually supportive with open trading (WTO, 2001, paragraph 6).

Contrary to the widespread view that it exists primarily to free trade, the WTO website insists that it exists to maintain a 'system of rules dedicated to open, fair and undistorted competition' (WTO, 2008). It also insists that it recognises that countries can and should protect human, animal or plant life and health, and protect their environments, though not in a discriminatory way, and has a Trade and Environment Committee. Nonetheless, it is not at all clear that environmental conservation and the WTO rules on trade liberalisation and fair competition are consistent in principle, and the committee has not set out to reconcile them in practice, where trade principles often take precedence.

In a very unequal world, there are potential conflicts between states' sovereign rights to set labour, health and environmental standards and the WTO's ideals of fair competition. The WTO cautiously recognises some basic labour standards set by the International Labour Organization (ILO), for example, ruling out child and forced labour, but less developed countries object to higher labour standards as a disguised form of protectionism (MacLaren, 2004). Similarly, the WTO allows for environmental standards to be set in multilateral environmental agreements and it recognises twenty such agreements that involve restrictions on trade. However, the WTO's objective of fair competition means that all WTO member states should be bound by the same rules. As a result, problems may arise in the WTO where some countries sign up to an environmental agreement but others do not, as this could mean different WTO member states being bound by different environmental standards (Brack, 2004). Nevertheless, just as some commentators have suggested that low labour standards should be

The polluter pays principle was introduced in Book 2, Chapter 8

UNCTAD, established in 1964 and headquartered in Geneva, Switzerland, is the organ of the UN General Assembly whose goal is to integrate developing countries into the world economy on an equitable basis.

construed as 'social dumping' (van Liemt, 2004), so low environmental standards in industry might be construed as a form of hidden subsidy, as the manufacturers have not had to pay the full costs of production. Even liberal environmentalism subscribes to the polluter pays principle. In our view, the insistence that the WTO regulates only trade and trade-related issues is both a de facto prioritisation of economic issues over other factors, and in contradiction with WTO's claims to pursue SD. It follows that either the WTO has to take action itself to negotiate harmonised environmental standards, or it needs to collaborate with those agencies, including UNEP, that are responsible for such standards. The problem would be compounded since WTO would also need to work with other bodies such as ILO, the World Bank, UNDP and the **United Nations Conference on Trade and Development (UNCTAD)** over environmental and social standards and how to integrate such standards into development policy. WTO's dominant focus on trade suggests that it may be preferable for it to cooperate with other international organisations that set environmental and social standards, rather than to set such standards itself.

Our analysis of the WTO, World Bank and IMF suggests that two modest proposals for change could begin to shift international economic governance towards a more balanced pursuit of profit, environmental sustainability, development and poverty reduction. First, the adoption of forms of governance more representative of the full range of states would surely help the IMF and the World Bank to take the needs of development and poverty reduction more seriously in their actions as well as their rhetoric. Second, closer partnership between the WTO and environment, health and labour standard setters would force the WTO into redefining 'open, fair and undistorted competition' (WTO, 2008) in a way that is consistent with the pursuit of environmental sustainability. In turn, the incorporation of environmental and social standards into WTO rules would add strong incentives to states to sign up to international standards.

These two proposals suggest that the concepts of problem solving and critical policy reform are best thought of as a spectrum rather than an 'either-or' distinction; the proposal of good governance seems at first glance to be limited to problem solving, but has the potential over time to open up political space to address more critical issues. Working out common standards is more critical, but the next section suggests that this might be moved towards problem solving by collaboration between organisations. Both proposals have the potential to increase the influence of actors currently excluded from international economic policy making, and in the process to promote values other than economic objectives. The next section discusses how this may be achieved by a restructuring within the UN.

5 A World Environment Organisation?

The twenty-first century presents us with challenges we have not faced before, and the institutions on which we have relied in the past may not be best equipped to serve us in the future. As Albert Einstein (1879–1955) once remarked, 'The significant problems we have cannot be solved at the same level of thinking with which we created them' (Einstein, undated). Sir Crispin Tickell (2003), commenting on environmental problems, has observed: 'Nothing is more difficult than learning to think differently. The problem ... goes to the root of how we run our society.'

Tickell is one of the proponents of a WEO. A proposal to create a WEO was made in the preparatory negotiations for the 1992 UNCED, although it failed to attract significant political support. The Commission on Sustainable Development was created as a compromise. Since then the idea of a WEO has gained support from many governments. In 2002 at the WSSD, the French President Jacques Chirac called for a WEO that would shift the focus of global governance away from economic concerns, achieving a balance between environmental and developmental issues (Figure 1.6). In 2007 Chirac announced that 46 nations supported the establishment of the WEO, including most member states of the EU as well as some countries from Latin America, Africa and Asia.

Figure 1.6
Former French President Jacques Chirac is one of the proponents of a WEO

In this section we will survey some of the arguments for and against a WEO, and explore some of the challenges such an organisation will have to overcome if it is to contribute to the solution of international environmental problems.

5.1 Some arguments for and against

Among the arguments put forward for a WEO are the following. A WEO could replace UNEP, which has been unable to effectively discharge its coordination mandate. A WEO could coordinate and rationalise the disparate international institutions that handle environmental issues, eliminating areas of duplication and addressing gaps in international environmental governance. Two types of gap may be identified. The first is omissions in existing multilateral environmental agreements. For example, greenhouse gas emissions from ships and aircraft are currently exempt from the Kyoto Protocol (Figure 1.7). A WEO could identify such gaps and prompt states to take measures to fill them, in this case perhaps in a post-Kyoto protocol to the Framework Convention on Climate Change.

A second type of gap arises from the current model of environmental governance whereby discrete environmental 'issues' are governed by separate multilateral environmental agreements, thus ignoring the complex interdependences within nature and between nature and society (*course theme 1*). One argument for a WEO is that a more holistic approach is needed, as how one environmental issue is governed may generate effects that have consequences for others. For example, separate international conventions address climate change, biodiversity loss and desertification, but there is no international mechanism that seeks to govern the connections between these different conventions (Figure 1.8). A WEO may provide a more interconnected model of governance that mimics the multifarious ecological connections between different environmental problems.

A WEO could also provide a technical focus for the centralisation of research, personnel training, coordinated global databases and national reporting by states, thus eliminating the administrative burden whereby states prepare separate reports for different environmental organisations. A WEO could also establish clear opportunities for developing countries to influence environmental governance, enabling a more high-level and focused consideration of the needs and interests of developing societies in policy implementation, something that UNEP, with its modest budget, has been unable to achieve. At a minimum a WEO would provide a single international venue that would raise the profile of environmental issues on the international agenda.

Figure 1.7

Carbon dioxide emissions from aircraft and ships are exempt from the Kyoto Protocol. Could a WEO help to fill such gaps in existing multilateral environmental agreements?

Figure 1.7a

New York's John F. Kennedy Airport

Figure 1.7b

The cruise ship Queen Elizabeth 2.

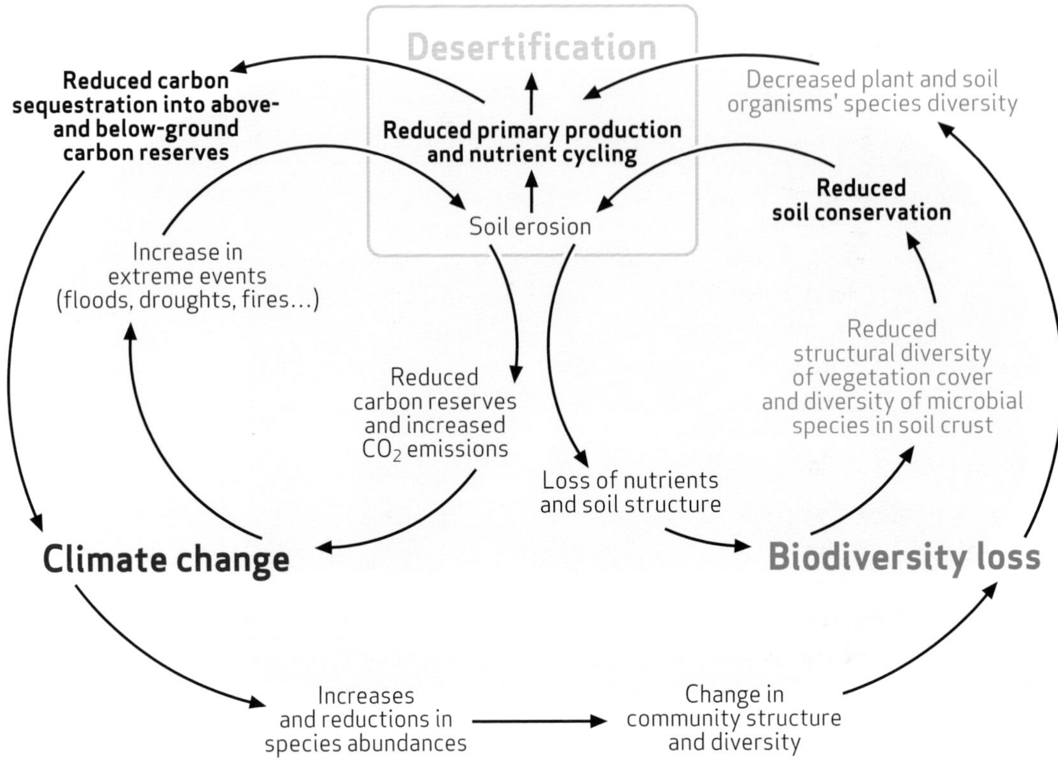

Notes: Green text: major components of biodiversity involved in the linkages.

Bold text: major services impacted by biodiversity losses.

The major components of biodiversity loss (in green) directly affect major dryland services (in bold). The inner loops connect desertification to biodiversity loss and climate change through soil erosion. The outer loop interrelates biodiversity loss and climate change. On the top section of the outer loop, reduced primary production and microbial activity reduce carbon sequestration and contribute to global warming. On the bottom section of the outer loop, global warming increases evapotranspiration, adversely affecting biodiversity; changes in community structure and diversity are also expected because different species will react differently to the elevated carbon dioxide (CO_2) concentrations.

Figure 1.8

Linkages and feedback loops between climate change, biodiversity loss and desertification. At present these issues are governed by the Framework Convention on Climate Change, 1992; the Convention on Biological Diversity, 1992; and the Convention to Combat Desertification, 1994 (Sources: MA, 2005a; UNEP, 2007, p. 372)

Box 1.2 presents three models of a WEO. These models are not exhaustive, nor are they mutually exclusive. If a WEO is created it could draw from all three models. However, the case for a WEO is by no means unchallenged.

Box 1.2 Possible models of a World Environment Organisation

Model 1: Dialogue

A WEO could serve as an arena where a plurality of interests could meet to develop a common basis for dialogue and agreement, with ECOSOC-type provisions for NGOs and other stakeholders to attend. According to this vision a WEO could function as an advisory expert panel of scientists, business people, NGO leaders and politicians, guiding and advising states on international environmental policies.

Model 2: Coordination

A WEO could function as an umbrella, a coordinating body streamlining the activities of different international legal agreements and exploiting the synergies between them. It could be organised into a general assembly taking decisions by qualified majority voting and adopting and overseeing treaties through an issue-based committee system. The committee structure could ensure coordination within different issue clusters. There could be an atmosphere committee handling climate change, ozone depletion and acid raid; a marine committee handling ocean pollution, sustainable fishery management and whaling; and so on. There could also be a regional committee structure handling coordination problems between, say, the main ecozones of the Earth. The general assembly would handle any coordination issues over interlinkages that the committee structure could not.

Model 3: Compliance

This model would function more along the lines of the WTO, as a quasi-legal body in which only states are represented. It would monitor implementation, resolve disputes and serve as a tough international enforcement agency with strong powers of enforcement and compliance. It would have the authority to levy fines and impose trade sanctions on states that violated international environmental law. This proposal would be deeply contested by many states, but if successful could provide a basis for a global governance system more focused on long-term sustainability.

The concept of an ecozone was introduced in Book 2, Chapter 5

Opponents of a WEO suggest that the functions of a WEO could be achieved by reforming the existing institutional apparatus. Some arguments focus on defending UNEP, which already provides a recognised and respected mechanism for addressing environmental problems. In this view, while there may be a case for UNEP to be improved and better funded, there is no case for it being replaced with a WEO. UNEP could be improved by making its stakeholder consultation processes more inclusive (Model 1 above). UNEP could be reformed to cluster existing agreements according to issue, by ecozone, and so on (Model 2 above). As for creating a WEO to ensure stronger implementation and compliance (Model 3), critics argue that states have the option of doing this under existing multilateral environmental agreements, but have not done so because they wish to maintain their sovereignty over their environment and natural resources. There is no basis for suggesting that a WEO would be more successful in overcoming the sovereignty problem than any other international environmental organisation has been.

It is also claimed that a WEO could lead to a centralised international environmental policy-making process dominated by developed countries. This is a concern of many member states of the Group of 77 developing countries (G77), most of which have been cautious of the idea of a WEO, fearing it could result in developed countries using environmental standards as a device to exert control of the resources of developing countries.

The G77 was discussed in Book 1, Chapters 1, 4 and 5, and Book 2, Chapters 7 and 9

Online Exercise 14

Now log on to the course website and complete Online Exercise 14: *The question of global environmental governance.*

Activity 1.5

From an environmental perspective we have suggested that there are two fundamental problems in global governance. First, there is no single organisation to oversee the implementation of multilateral environmental agreements. Second, global governance on the environment is normatively weaker than those that govern the global economy. To what extent might a WEO address these two problems?

Much depends on institutional design, but in principle a WEO could help to solve the first problem by promoting a less fragmented and more integrated system of global governance on the environment. However, whether it could resolve the tensions between environmental governance and economic governance depends on the relationship between a WEO on the one hand, and the WTO and BWIs on the other. We now pursue this question, although again for reasons of space our analysis is confined to the WTO.

5.2 The relationship between a World Environment Organisation and the WTO

A WEO could act as a counterweight against the current model of governance adopted by the WTO. By speaking with a single clear voice on environmental issues a WEO would be better placed to promote environmental standards in global governance, and to exert direct influence over the WTO, than the current model of environmental governance, where responsibility for environmental issues is dispersed over various international organisations.

Nevertheless, a WEO that dealt solely with environmental issues without reference to economic issues would represent only a modest institutional balancing act. The result could be to further isolate environmental issues from global economic policy, leading to a more sharply polarised model of global governance in which two major international institutions – a WTO and a WEO – vie for supremacy. Creating a WEO that leaves the WTO in charge of international trade and investment law and a WEO in charge of international environmental law would not solve this problem, merely recast it.

One view is that a WEO could only be effective if it were set up to complement the WTO and with equal legitimacy in its governance. Thinking in these terms clarifies which of the three models in Box 1.2 should be adopted. Model 1, with its limitation to dialogue, would never be effective. Model 2, coordinating environmental policy and standards, could claim to offer the WTO a coherent internationally agreed set of environmental standards that could be integrated into WTO rules. Model 3 would be unlikely to command international support, but would not be needed if the WTO adopted those standards and used them in its own enforcement. A collaboration between a Model 2 WEO and the WTO could potentially solve the WTO's need for authoritative environmental standards and the persistent problem that states need not sign up to, or actively implement, multilateral environmental agreements. Roy MacLaren summed it up as follows:

> The basic question abides: Can a multilateral trade organisation serve as a mechanism to impose sanctions for the development, monitoring, and enforcement of internationally agreed standards? The advocates, almost entirely in developed countries, continue to answer an awkward yes.
>
> (MacLaren, 2004, p. 268)

The precautionary principle and the principle of common but differentiated responsibilities were introduced in Book 1, Chapter 1 and discussed in Book 2, Chapter 8

Setting up such a WEO would only be a start in reconciling environment and trade. It would be an intensely difficult intellectual and political problem to develop environmental principles, such as the polluter pays principle and the precautionary principle, into operational standards. States would need to agree on the practical implementation of principles, such as common but differentiated responsibilities. Since less developed countries have resisted adopting standards which would act as barriers to trade, one approach would be to agree high standards for developed countries and transitional lower standards for less developed countries.

However, this would first require political acceptance from developed countries, many of which would oppose such an endeavour. Establishing a WEO would involve some politically tricky negotiations. We now examine some of the issues that might arise if such a round of negotiations were to be held. We consider the basis on which a global bargain may be formed using forests as a case study.

6 Towards a global bargain?

Throughout the 1950s and 1960s most of the European colonies in Africa and Asia were granted independence. In the 1960s these countries coalesced at the UN as the G77, a group which now represents well over a hundred developing countries, ranging from oil exporters and newly industrialising countries through to the low-income least developed countries. Their main concerns were, indeed remain to this day, the major inequalities and uneven distributions of power in the international economic system (*course theme 2*). In the 1970s the G77 presented to the UN a political programme for a New International Economic Order (NIEO) to overcome these inequalities. Their arguments express a set of problems that still exists and which will have to be addressed if environmental concerns are to be given increased priority.

6.1 The New International Economic Order

The NIEO advocated a macro-level restructuring of the global economic system to yield a fairer distribution of the world's economic and natural resources. The G77 sought to use the control of developing countries over their natural resources as bargaining leverage with the developed countries. The G77 argued that if the developing countries were to continue to supply their natural resources to the developed countries, the latter should agree to supply the developing countries with transfers of finance and technology and to agree to external debt relief or forgiveness.

Although these negotiations led to the developing countries receiving some limited financial and technical assistance, these countries were ultimately unsuccessful in their demands for a NIEO. Attempts by the G77 to link the supply of natural resources and commodities to the developed countries in exchange for the supply of manufactured products and advanced technology failed because developing countries had relatively little to offer in exchange for what they wanted. The developing countries simply did not have the economic power to leverage substantial concessions from the developed countries (Renninger, 1989). Although the developing countries had a strong ethical argument – most of the world's population lives in Africa, Latin America and Asia, while most of the world's wealth is owned by interests in Europe and North America – the developed countries were unwilling to surrender relative advantages in international trade and finance in order to help other countries.

The political failure of this initiative is hardly surprising: in many respects it was a *critical* proposal, which would have reformed global governance so as to benefit poor countries at the expense of richer ones, who used their political and economic power to block the NIEO. However, if the ethical issues of relieving environmental degradation, poverty and inequality are to be solved, a way will have to be found to bring about change with just these effects.

By the late 1970s the NIEO debate had waned. But although the concerns of developing countries had receded into the background in international diplomacy, they never disappeared. Increasing international concern at global environmental degradation has ushered in a new phase in international relations that has given a new lease of life to the NIEO concerns voiced by the G77 in the 1970s (Humphreys, 1996). This became apparent during the negotiations for the 1992 UNCED in Rio de Janeiro. While these negotiations agreed conventions on climate change and biodiversity there was no consensus to agree a forests convention.

6.2 Conserving the world's forests: who should pay?

During the UNCED forest negotiations the G77, led by Malaysia, wished to establish a bargaining linkage between forest conservation and NIEO demands such as external debt relief and increased aid transfers (although the NIEO was not mentioned by name). The negotiations may be viewed crudely as a price negotiation in which the G77 stated that it would not agree any binding forest conservation measures unless it received economic concessions from the developed countries in return. Insisting that all issues be settled in a comprehensive package, the G77 argued for a global forest fund and for technology transfers to help developing countries achieve sustainable forest management

Opportunity cost refers to the alternative that must be foregone when an economic resource is used.

(Humphreys, 1996). The G77 introduced the concept of *compensation for opportunity cost foregone*. **Opportunity cost** is a concept that has its origins in economic theory. It refers to the alternative that must be foregone when an economic resource is used. So if a resource is used to produce Good A it cannot then be used to produce Good B. By invoking the concept the G77 asserted that tropical forest countries should be financially compensated if they were to agree to conserve rather than exploit their forests. As the Malaysian Prime Minister, Mahathir bin Mohamad, commented: 'If it is in the interests of the rich that we do not cut down our trees then they must compensate us for the loss of income' (Mahathir, 1992). In effect the G77 raised the price of forest conservation during the UNCED forest negotiations, a price that the developed countries were unwilling to pay.

The UNCED forest negotiations did not, therefore, focus exclusively on forests, and saw protracted deliberations on economic concerns of salience to the developing countries. This pattern has continued in the post-UNCED era and is not limited to forests. The developing countries regularly introduce demands for increased finance and technology transfers in international negotiations on other environmental issues, such as biological diversity, desertification and climate change, and the developed countries regularly decline to meet these demands. This raises the question of how effective the UN and other international organisations can be if different states wish to attain very different objectives (Figure 1.9).

Figure 1.9
United Nations: divided world. International institutions are more effective when member states share agreement on broad policy objectives

Activity 1.6

Should developed countries pay for forest conservation in the tropics? What ethical arguments might you use if you were a negotiator for the G77 at the UN?

The question of responsibility enters into any ethical debate on this subject (*course theme 6*). Developing countries have invoked the principle of *common but differentiated responsibilities*, noting the different historical contributions of countries to deforestation: while much primary tropical forest remains there is very little of the original extent of forest cover in Europe and North America. The G77 has argued that the developed countries have an ethical responsibility to pay for conserving the world's tropical forests not only because of past deforestation, but because if they do not, deforestation is inevitable. At present forest owners and tropical forest governments have a rational economic incentive to deforest. This argument relates to the concept of opportunity cost. At present tropical deforestation takes place because it yields more financial benefits for forest owners and governments than forest conservation. But these actors will rationally opt for forest conservation if they can receive more for conserving their forests than for cutting them down.

In 2007 the governments of two South American countries offered to enter into legally binding forest conservation agreements in exchange for huge financial transfers from developed countries. The government of Ecuador stated that it would desist from deforestation in order to exploit its Amazonian oil fields if it were to receive international assistance. President Rafael Correa commented, 'Ecuador doesn't ask for charity but does ask that the international community share in the sacrifice and compensates us with at least half of what our country would receive, in recognition of the environmental benefits that would be generated by keeping this oil underground.' The sum mentioned was $350 million per annum (Environment News Service, 2007). The same year the government of Guyana offered to protect its entire expanse of rainforest if the British government would undertake to provide the country with the resources needed to achieve SD and lift its population out of poverty (Howden, 2007).

At first glance it might appear that Ecuador and Guyana are asking to receive money for nothing (Figure 1.10). However, if the debate is framed as one of payment for environmental services it makes more sense. Conserving the world's remaining tropical forests will provide environmental services such as soil conservation, rainfall and habitat conservation, which will benefit the host countries as well as, indirectly, other countries. It will also enable the conservation of a major carbon sink. Most industrial carbon emissions take place in the developed

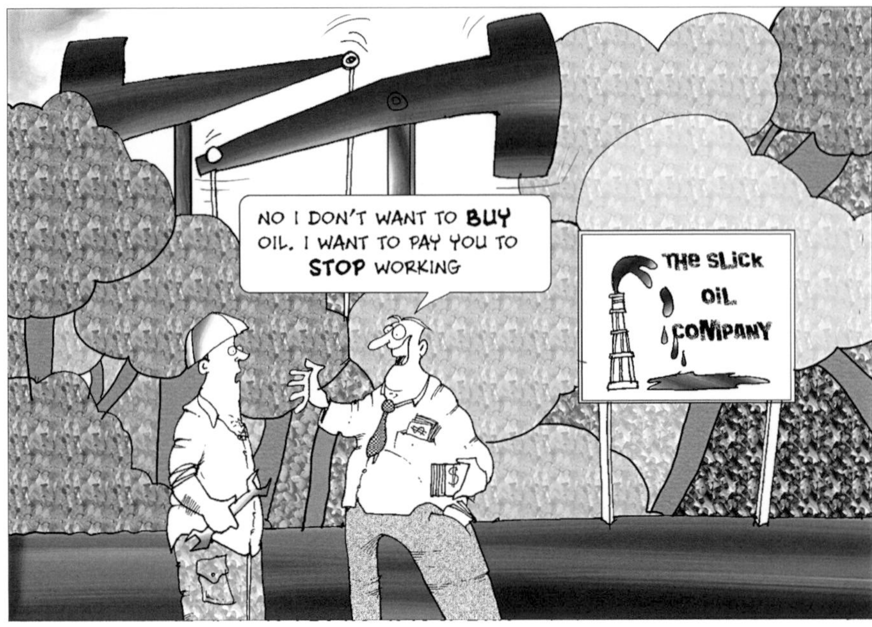

Figure 1.10
Money for nothing? Paying Amazonian countries not to exploit their oil reserves may conserve vital environmental services and stimulate more sustainable forms of development

countries, but when emissions from deforestation are included, then Indonesia and Brazil become the world's third and fourth largest emitters of carbon dioxide (CO_2), after the USA and China (*Economist*, 2006). A global system of payments for environmental services could enable these countries to progress towards SD without deforesting.

7 The role of the state

The discussion in the previous section makes clear that states and coalitions of states will remain absolutely central in future environmental diplomacy and international institution building. Although there has been some ceding of rule-making authority from intergovernmental organisations to the private sector, as the Global Compact illustrates, any future reforms to global governance will require the active involvement of the world's states. International institutions reflect the values of states, in particular powerful states, and their societies. As John Ruggie (1983) has argued, the post-war global economic order can be seen as a compromise between two demands. The first was the demand from societies in North America and Europe for domestic social and economic stability following the trauma of World War II. The second was the desire of the dominant post-war power, the USA, to establish a liberal, multilateral free-trading system to drive global economic growth. Ruggie referred to this as 'embedded liberalism'.

Can the state play a role in creating a more environmentally sustainable system of global governance? There are different views here. Critical thinkers question whether the Hobbesian state has the capability to provide security for its citizens against global environmental threats that traverse political borders. For example, Matthew Paterson (2001) argues that the state is embedded within global power structures that routinely generate environmental degradation. Paterson emphasises the role of the state in facilitating and promoting the expansion of global capitalism and hence driving environmental and social problems. He argues that there are structures that underpin the actions of social actors, who can choose to reproduce these structures or to challenge them. Capitalism is defined in the Marxist sense, with labour and the environment commodified and exploited in order to expropriate surplus value for companies that in a competitive world economy are forced to expand and increase their profitability in order to survive. Social and environmental effects are secondary to capital accumulation and profit maximisation.

The Hobbesian notion of the state was introduced in Book 1, Chapter 5

Paterson (2001) takes a critical view of the state; he sees it as part of the problem of environmental degradation and doubts that it can be reformed. Instead, he envisages a central role for active resistance. Resistance involves creating new forms of governance and social spaces that exclude the state and transnational corporations, challenging established discourses, promoting local-level action and creating organised networks of grassroots groups that demand that local environments be managed by and for local people. Resistance, Paterson suggests, is an expression of power that can transform global governance.

Capitalist social relations have proved to be the most efficient form of industrialisation and development. Capitalism has had a broad and deep impact on the environment simply by virtue of being the most successful form of organisation that provides for human needs. Whether capitalism is a huge constraint on sustainability or a force that can be regulated and harnessed to generate a more sustainable world is a keenly contested subject. Environmental activists and green parties are divided on whether they should work with the state and capitalism. In the 1980s the German Green Party (*die Grünen*) was divided between the fundamentalists (*Fundis*) and the realists (*Realos*) on their political strategy. The *Fundis* argued that the greens should maintain the purity of their values and ideological beliefs by seeking change outside the state, refusing to stand for elections or cooperate with business. The *Realos* argued that if change was to happen it could only begin by working with and through those institutions that held political and economic power. The *Realos* asserted that the state could be reformed, while the *Fundis* disagreed, seeing the state as part of the problem (Doherty, 1992).

Both factions agreed a major transformation in society was necessary, though they disagreed on how this transformation should be realised. Similar debates continue to take place in the world's green parties (Box 1.3).

Box 1.3 When the grandchildren tell our story

Generations from now, parents will tell their children the story of our times. They will tell them about the Great Transformation; the shift that civilization made from its growth phase, which had continued since early times, to a new, mature state, where the total of materials, energy and consequent waste was maintained within steady, sustainable volumes. This change had to happen. Human activity was already stretching planetary limits, and the systems were in place to fully double that activity every 20 years. The story told about our times will be one of praise; telling how well our generation recognized the challenge and rose to meet it, or it will be a tale of great sorrow; telling how those alive today denied that it was our task to find a stable state. Whether the story the children hear is one of triumph or of sorrow depends on how soon we recognize the challenge and accept the historic responsibility.

Source: Nickerson and Dillman, 2006 (Green Party of Canada advertisement)

The principles of intragenerational and intergenerational equity were introduced in Book 1, Chapter 1 and discussed in Book 1, Chapter 6

John Barry and Robyn Eckersley (2005) argue that acknowledging the modern state operates in an instrumental manner that serves particular economic interests does not mean that it cannot be rendered sustainable in the future, serving different interests and promoting different values. In this view only a strong state can control transnational movements of capital, provide a regulatory framework for business that is grounded in environmental ethics, support sustainability initiatives at the local level and promote the principles of intragenerational and intergenerational equity. It may be argued that it is unrealistic, maybe even naïve, to suggest that environmental degradation can be arrested using an institution such as the state which, so far, has failed to stem environmental degradation. In response it may be asked that if publicly accountable bodies such as the state are not going to represent the long-term interests of humanity then who, precisely, will do this. Those who defend the state as an agent of sustainability argue that it is not the state per se that is the problem; it is its penetration by neoliberal values and its near exclusive focus on the economy. With this viewpoint the modern state can be transformed to become an agent that regulates for the common good of present and future generations (Figure 1.11).

Figure 1.11
The US flag has been adopted and adapted by various political causes in history. The green stars and stripes emerged from the North American ecology movement in the 1970s. The 'corporate stars and stripes' swaps the stars for the logos of some American business corporations. It was designed by the Canadian-based anti-consumerist group Adbusters to claim that the US federal government represents the interests of big business, rather than the citizens or individual states of the USA. The two images symbolise some of the competing demands that different actors make on the US federal government

Activity 1.7

In this view a transition from a neoliberal state to a green state is possible; some would say essential. How might this come about? You might find it helpful to return to Ruggie's notion of 'embedded liberalism' at the start of this section.

Ruggie argued that the post-war international order of 'embedded liberalism' arose from a combination of two demands: social demands in developed countries for domestic stability, and the role of the USA in promoting an international free-trade system. The advent of global environmental problems poses an ethical challenge to embedded liberalism, challenging it as a set of economic relations that is compatible with these two demands. Environmental problems, in particular anthropogenic climate change, are likely to lead to major instability, economically and politically. Following on from Ruggie we would expect a transformation of global governance to come about when two conditions are met. First, a significant shift takes place in state–society relations, with citizens pressuring national governments to deliver stronger international institutions guided by environmental norms. Second, the world's most powerful countries – and the USA is as important today as it was in 1945 – demand the creation of a new international order dedicated to the provision of long-term environmental stability.

8 Conclusion

We are living through an historical moment when we must decide which values will prevail in global governance. Abolishing all international institutions is not a serious option. We need rules to govern the world. The question is: what set of rules? We have argued that a more or less coherent set of rules has been agreed to govern the neoliberal global economy, but other rules incorporating environmental norms are possible. Using the debate on a WEO, we suggested that creating new rules for environmental problems that ignore the complex interconnections between economic governance and environmental governance will not provide an international institutional framework that will enable more effective environmental policies. What is needed is an integrated body of international law that provides a clear set of rules to govern the global economic system so as to promote environmental conservation and SD.

Given the challenges we face it is, perhaps, easy to feel powerless, believing that the fate of the global environment is out of our hands. But doing nothing in the face of international environmental problems is not an option we consider in this course. Here we may note the words of the political philosopher Edmund Burke (1729–1797): 'No-one could make a greater mistake than he who did nothing because he could do only a little' (Burke, undated). It is, of course, far easier to imagine the principles that will guide more sustainable global governance than it is to imagine the processes and mechanisms through which change will occur. Are huge changes necessary, or will reforming existing institutions suffice? Will change be evolutionary, or will environmental problems worsen, leading to sudden, almost revolutionary, changes in global governance?

One thing that emerges from this chapter is that global governance is a product of many actors and processes. Reform at the global level will not take place unless there are changes at other levels of governance. The demand for change may come from a range of actors, including business, scientists, local authorities, social and environmental NGOs and green parties. Central to this debate is the role of the state. International institutions are created by states, and they reflect the dominant values and beliefs of states in the international system. We have suggested that changes to the state and the values it serves may take place if there is a shift in state–society relations. So in one sense the onus for change lies with individual citizens (*course theme 6*). You will explore the role that 'ecological citizens' can play in Chapter 5 of this book.

First, however, we wish to look in another direction. Having 'looked up' to global governance we shall now 'look down' in Chapter 2 and explore the role that environmental movements and NGOs may play in promoting more effective environmental policies.

Audio 7

Now listen to Audio 7: *Capacity building for international negotiations.*

References

Annan, K. (1999) UN Press release SG/SM/6881, 'Secretary-general proposes Global Compact on human rights, labour, environment, in address to World Economic Forum in Davos' [online], 1 February, http://www.un.org/News/Press/docs/1999/19990201.sgsm6881.html (Accessed 18 September 2008).

Barry, J. and Eckersley, R. (2005) 'W(h)ither the green state?' in Barry, J. and Eckersley, R. (eds) *The State and the Global Ecological Crisis*, Cambridge, MA, MIT Press.

Brack, D. (2004) 'Trade and the environment' in Hocking, B. and McGuire, S. (eds) *Trade Politics* (2nd edn), London, Routledge, pp. 223–37.

Burke, E. (undated) *The Quotations Page* [online], http://www.quotationspage.com/quotes/Edmund_Burke (Accessed 25 September 2008).

Coleman, D. (2003) 'The United Nations and transnational corporations: from an inter-nation to a "beyond-state" model of engagement', *Global Society: Journal of Interdisciplinary International Relations*, vol. 17, no. 4, pp. 339–57.

Cox, R. W. (1986) 'Social forces, states and world orders: beyond international relations theory' in Keohane, R. O. (ed.) *Neorealism and its Critics*, New York, Columbia University Press.

Derber, C. (2002) *People Before Profit: The New Globalisation in an Age of Terror, Big Money and Economic Crisis*, London, Souvenir Press.

Doherty, B. (1992) 'The Fundi-Realo controversy: an analysis of four European green parties', *Environmental Politics*, vol. 1, no. 1, pp. 95–120.

Eckersley, R. (2004) 'The big chill: the WTO and multilateral environmental agreements', *Global Environmental Politics*, vol. 4, no. 2, pp. 24–50.

Economist, The (2006) 'So hard to see the wood for the trees' [online], 19 December, http://www.economist.com/world/international/displaystory.cfm?story_id=10329203 (Accessed 10 January 2007).

Einstein, A. (undated) *The Quotations Page* [online], http://www.quotationspage.com/quotes/Albert_Einstein/31 (Accessed 18 September 2008).

Elliott, L. (2004) *The Global Politics of the Environment* (2nd edn), Basingstoke, Palgrave Macmillan.

Environment News Service (2007) 'Ecuador seeks compensation to leave Amazon oil undisturbed' [online], 24 April, http://www.ens-newswire.com/ens/apr2007/2007-04-24-04.asp (Accessed 3 December 2007).

Gill, S. (1995) 'Globalisation, market civilisation and disciplinary neoliberalism', *Millennium: Journal of International Studies*, vol. 24, no. 3, pp. 399–423.

Gill, S. (2002) *Power and Resistance in the New World Order*, London, Palgrave Macmillan.

Horten, D. (1995) *When Corporations Rule the World*, London, Earthscan.

Howden, D. (2007) 'Take over our rainforest: Guyana's extraordinary offer to Britain to save one of the world's most important carbon sinks', *The Independent*, 24 November, pp. 1–3.

Humphreys, D. (1996) *Forest Politics: The Evolution of International Cooperation*, London, Earthscan.

Imber, M. (1993) 'Too many cooks?: The post-Rio reform of the United Nations', *International Affairs*, vol. 69, no. 1, pp. 55–70.

Independent Evaluation Group (IEG) (2008) 'Environmental sustainability: an evaluation of World Bank Group support' [online], http://siteresources.worldbank.org/EXTENENVIRONMENT/Resources/EvalSumm.pdf (Accessed 15 October 2008).

International Monetary Fund (IMF) (2008a) 'What is the Poverty Reduction and Growth Facility?' [online], http://www.imf.org/external/np/exr/facts/prgf.htm (Accessed 15 October 2008).

International Monetary Fund (IMF) (2008b) 'Reform of IMF quotas and voice: responding to changes in the global economy' [online], http://www.imf.org/external/np/exr/ib/2008/040108.htm (Accessed 15 October 2008).

Lafferty, W. M. and Eckerberg, K. (eds) (1998) *From the Earth Summit to Local Agenda 21: Working Towards Sustainable Development*, London, Earthscan.

MacLaren, R. (2004) 'Integrating environment and labour into the World Trade Organization' in Kirton, J. and Trebilcock, M. (eds) *Hard Choices, Soft Law; Voluntary Standards in Global Trade, Environment and Social Governance*, Aldershot, Ashgate, pp. 266–9.

Mahathir, B. M. (1992) 'Speech by the prime minister of Malaysia, Dato' Seri Dr Mahathir bin Mohamad at the official opening of the Second Ministerial Conference of Developing Countries on Environment and Development, Kuala Lumpur, on Monday, 27 April 1992', London, High Commissioner for Malaysia.

Millennium Ecosystem Assessment (MA) (2005) *Ecosystems and Human Well-being: Synthesis*, Washington, DC, Island Press.

Mullally, G. (1998) 'Ireland: does the road from Rio lead back to Brussels?' in Lafferty, W. M. and Eckerberg, K. (eds) *From the Earth Summit to Local Agenda 21: Working Towards Sustainable Development*, London, Earthscan.

Nickerson, M. and Dillman, D. (2006) 'When the grandchildren tell our story', *Adbusters: Journal of the Mental Environment*, vol. 14, no. 5, September/October.

Paterson, M. (2001) *Understanding Global Environmental Politics*, London, Palgrave Macmillan.

Prasad, E., Rogoff, K., Wei. S.-J. and Ayhan Lose, M. (2003) 'Effects of financial globalisation on developing countries: some empirical evidence', IMF Working Paper.

Renninger, J. P. (1989) 'The failure to launch global negotiations at the 11th Special Session of the General Assembly' in Kaufmann, J. (ed.) *Effective Negotiation: Case Studies in Conference Diplomacy*, Dordrecht, Netherlands, Martinus Nijhoff.

Ruggie, J. (1983) 'International regimes, transactions, and change: embedded liberalism in the postwar economic order' in Krasner, S. D. (ed.) *International Regimes*, Ithaca, NY, Cornell University Press.

Stiglitz, J. (2002) *Globalisation and its Discontents*, New York, W. W. Norton.

Streck, C. (2001) 'The Global Environment Facility: a role model for international governance?', *Global Environmental Politics*, vol. 1, no. 2, pp. 71–94.

Tickell, C. (2003) 'The United Nations, multilateralism and the environment', St Edmund's College Law Society Lecture, Cambridge, 3 May 2003.

United Nations (UN) (1945) *Charter of the United Nations* [online], http://www.un.org/aboutun/charter (Accessed 21 September 2008).

United Nations (UN) (1948) *Universal Declaration of Human Rights* [online], http://www.unhchr.ch/udhr/download/index.htm (Accessed 21 September 2008).

United Nations Economic and Social Commission for Asia and the Pacific (2008) 'What is good governance?' [online], http://www.unescap.org/pdd/prs/projectactivities/ongoing/gg/governance.asp (Accessed 15 October 2008).

United Nations Environment Programme (UNEP) (2007) *Global Environment Outlook 4; Environment for Development*, Valetta, Malta, Progress Press/UNEP.

van Liemt, G. (2004) 'Trade and human rights: the issue of minimum labour standards' in Hocking, B. and McGuire, S. (eds) *Trade Politics* (2nd edn), London, Routledge, pp. 238–48.

Willetts, P. (1996) 'From Stockholm to Rio and beyond: the impact of the environmental movement on the United Nations consultative arrangements for NGOs', *Review of International Studies*, vol. 22, no. 1, pp. 57–80.

World Bank (1998) 'Our dream is a world free of poverty' [online], http://go.worldbank.org/4DO5SXV2H0 (Accessed 15 October 2008).

World Trade Organization (WTO) (1994) 'Agreement establishing the WTO, signed at Marrakesh' [online], http://www.wto.org/english/docs_e/legal_e/04-wto.pdf (Accessed 15 October 2008).

World Trade Organization (WTO) (2001) 'Ministerial declaration' [online], http://www.wto.org/english/thewto_e/minint_e/min01_e/mindecl_e.htm (Accessed 15 October 2008).

World Trade Organization (WTO) (2007) 'Understanding the WTO: basics' [online], http://www.wto.org/english/thewto_e/whatis_e/tif_e/fact2_e.htm (Accessed 15 October 2008).

World Trade Organization (WTO) (2008) 'Understanding the WTO: principles of the trading system' [online], http://www.wto.org/english/thewto_/whatis_e/tif_e/fact2_e.htm (Accessed 15 October 2008).

World Trade Organization (WTO) (undated) 'The General Agreement on Tariffs and Trade (GATT 1947)' [online], http://www.wto.org/english/docs_e/legal_e/gatt47_02_e.htm (Accessed 16 November 2008).

Chapter 2

Look down: the changing environmental movement

Piya Pangsapa and Mark J. Smith

Contents

1 Introduction

This chapter continues the course's exploration of what can, and should, be done to improve environmental policy for the future (*course question 4*) by looking in diametrically the opposite direction from the previous chapter. Where that looked 'up' to the important international organisations that shape our world, this chapter looks 'down' to initiatives built from 'below' by individuals and groups from what social scientists call 'civil society', that is from outside the organisations that make up the state and the economy. Attempts by individuals to become active citizens, take responsibility and influence events, individually or in association with others, are central to *course theme 6*, and often involve contention over values and knowledge (*course theme 3*).

At first glance, it may seem surprising to seek for change among people who, by definition, lack access to the powers of either the state or economic organisations. However, in the case of the environment it is perfectly reasonable, since all the issues considered in this course were originally framed and put on to national and international political agendas by just such individuals and groups, contributing to what we now refer to as 'the environmental movement'. As has been mentioned previously in the course, for example, in Book 2, Chapter 9, a change occurred in the North in about 1970, when a range of ideas that had previously been regarded as unimportant, even eccentric, began to be more broadly accepted by society, and by governments, as both related and significant and as requiring policy response. For example, in 1970 US President Nixon brought fifteen existing agencies together into a unified Environmental Protection Agency (EPA). It was tasked with cleaning up air, water and land pollution, becoming for a decade or more the leading environmental agency in the world; with 17,000 employees and a huge range of laws and regulations, it is still a major influence. If the fragmented efforts of environmentalists could achieve such a momentous change in outlook in 1970, perhaps they can do so again, especially since the environmental movement has many more sympathisers now, has much better access to many states and even has influence within, and on, business organisations.

A **non-governmental organisation (NGO)** is a non-profit and voluntary citizens' organisation, with the status of a legal entity, that pursues goals shared by its members and supporters.

In general terms, the environmental movement is commonly understood as being made up of a set of actors, including individuals, informal groups from a locality, networked special interest groups, national organisations and transnational conglomerates, many in the form of a **non-governmental organisation (NGO)**, i.e. a non-profit and voluntary citizens' organisation, with the status of a legal entity, that pursues goals shared by its members and supporters. The movement's aims may range from minimising human impacts on nature to preserving only the environmental services that are indispensable to human survival. Its methods may range from direct action protests in opposition to state or business initiatives, through to persuasion, collaboration and infiltration. Its style may range from hard science, through sophisticated public relations to ascetic spirituality.

A problem for any analysis of the potential of the environmental movement to stimulate further change is that it has always been, and remains, extremely heterogeneous, always undergoing major transformations over time (*course theme* 5). These changes have been so profound that since the 1990s they have repeatedly raised questions as to whether environmentalism should still be conceived as a grassroots, participatory movement (Diani and Rambaldo, 2007). Looking at the best known Northern national and international environmental organisations, with their shifts towards professionalisation, institutionalisation and concern with cultural production rather than political representation (Jamison, 2001), it could be argued that since the 1990s, grassroots participation has ceased to be an appropriate descriptor of their activities. However, in the same period new forms of primarily locally based, and often quite radical, environmental activism developed (Rootes, 2003) and, as JoAnn Carmin (1999) argued, often reinvigorated environmental action at the national and possibly international level.

Many publications have sought to document and classify the full range of the movement (for example, Schlosberg, 1999; Wissenburg, 1998), but in this short chapter we will take a more selective approach, dealing only with what we characterise as the 'mainstream' movement, that is the high-profile NGOs that dominate media attention in the North (Section 2); the Environmental Justice Movement (EJM), a recent development that we think has made a distinct practical and theoretical contribution towards building a more effective and principled movement (Section 3); and very recent indications of the problems and strategies of environmentalists in the fast developing economies of Asia (Section 4).

To sharpen our assessment of the potential of each of these parts of the environmental movement to promote change, we use several concepts developed in the broader field of social movement studies. Use of concepts and evidence from a range of theoretical approaches helps explain what makes movements more or less successful, and anticipates the possibility that to become more successful environmentalists may need to make alliances with other social movements. Concepts from social movement theory are introduced in Section 2 in relation to the mainstream environmental movement, then applied in Sections 3 and 4 to the environmental justice movement in the US and Asian cases – with you being asked to do progressively more of the application in activities. In Section 5 we sum up the findings of the chapter and point to the implications for other levels of governance as well as for movement organisations.

1.1 Learning outcomes

This chapter should enable you to:

- widen and deepen your understanding of the environmental movement
- understand and use major concepts from the theory of social movements
- assess what factors contribute to the success or failure of citizen initiatives
- identify some criteria to assess how the environmental movement should change in future.

2 Analysing the environmental movement

This section addresses two questions: what is meant by the term 'the environmental movement'?; and how can concepts from the theory of social movements help make sense of its variety and varying effectiveness?

Activity 2.1

Think back to the issues discussed in Book 2 of this course. Can you recall examples of civil society actors influencing the framing of problems, debates about policy or the resolution of issues?

Although the course focuses on policy, and hence on activity within and between states, civil society actors played a role in almost all the issues discussed. Some major examples are:

- In discussing population, the role of neo-Malthusians, whether named individuals like the Ehrlichs or organisations like the Optimum Population Trust, was crucial in framing population as a problem, even as 'a bomb'.
- In India, the Chipko movement started with non-violent direct action to prevent tree felling and moved on to political and legal efforts to defend rural people from losing access to forests.

- The citizens of Cochabamba took direct action to resist water privatisation.
- Biodiversity protection involves a range of major international organisations like the World Conservation Union and the World Wide Fund for Nature (WWF), as well as more specific groups like the Forest People's Program.
- Book 2, Chapter 6 suggests that Rachel Carson single handedly launched the modern environmental movement in 1962, and goes on to show that organic and fair trade campaigns have had significant effects.
- Perhaps most crucially, Book 2, Chapter 7 both identifies how non-state actors created the climate in which the United Nations (UN) decided to address environmental issues in 1972, and identifies a more recent trend away from 'government', in which the state takes independent responsibility, towards 'governance', in which a wider range of actors, including many from civil society, are involved in policy development and implementation. In practice, this may involve linkages, including partnerships, that blur the boundaries between state, civil society and economic organisations.

Even this short list confirms that civil society interventions in environmental policy making are very varied, in the nature of the participants, the way they are organised, their objectives and their methods. While only a fraction of civil society organisations see themselves as specifically 'environmental', even that fraction consists of a very large number of highly varied entities. Marcel Wissenburg (1998) argues that the environmental movement is divided on four major levels (beliefs about the relation between society and nature, values to be pursued in future, political approach, and policy preferences), each of which has four to seven alternative positions, combining to distinguish dozens, even hundreds, of possible combinations of beliefs, values and policy preferences. However, many movement entities are small, short lived and little known so, although he also points to great diversity, David Schlosberg (1999) argues that a relatively small number of big organisations concerned with environmental preservation, including Greenpeace, Friends of the Earth and the WWF, plus major national organisations in developed countries, command most media attention, and are treated as if they were the movement. Greenpeace is particularly expert in staging protests in ways that attract media attention, as shown in Figure 2.1. This chapter identifies this subset as 'the mainstream environmental movement' and contrasts it with just one of the alternative approaches, the 'environmental justice movement' (EJM).

Figure 2.1
New social movement activism in Europe

Activity 2.2

Think about some environmentalist organisations you are familiar with, list some of the ways they vary and consider how effective they are in achieving their objectives.

Rather than address this question directly, the next subsection considers social movements more broadly, before returning to consider the mainstream environmental movement. In Activity 2.3, you will be asked to relate the organisations you are familiar with to the discussion of social movements.

2.1 Social movements: old and new

A **social movement** is a sustained, collective challenge to established elites, practices or values, with the aim of bringing about change.

In order to identify concepts that can help in the analysis of the changing environmental movement, we turn to a broad literature in social sciences concerned with the analysis of social movements, mainly in the context of affluent democratic societies. A **social movement** is a sustained, collective challenge to established elites, practices or values, with the aim of bringing about change. Participants in a social movement often share a grievance, and campaign for change that will eliminate it. One of the first social movements to attract attention, from its opponents and from scholars, was the labour movement of the nineteenth century. Stimulated by the harsh conditions of workers in the factories and fields of rapidly industrialising countries, it campaigned for better working conditions and higher wages. Fighting over many decades and in many countries, this movement achieved substantial successes, peaking in the Bretton Woods era described in Book 2, Chapter 9. However, it has lost ground in the developed world, though it is being re-created in the newly industrialising countries of today.

After 1945 a wider set of social movements came to the fore and was identified as 'new social movements' (NSMs). **New social movement theory**, developed in the 1970s and 1980s by theorists such as Jürgen Habermas (1981) and Alberto Melucci (1989), was concerned with new grievances and collective interests, values and identities (Miller, 2000). These new grievances relate to the environment, gender, civil rights and disability. NSMs seek to articulate a common identity and defend an autonomous space in society. Because they are concerned with challenging values and assumptions of citizens as much as with specific campaigns, and concerned more with identity and lifestyle than with material benefits, NSMs are often described as **postmaterialist**. As a result of their direct action tactics, they were initially thought of as outsiders rather than insiders in terms of influencing state policy. The contrast reflects the difference between trade unions that were by then embedded in policy communities and national economic plans, while environmental groups were more prone to oppositional protests. However, since the 1980s many environmental NGOs (as well as elements of other NSMs) have themselves developed a political insider role while unions have largely lost influence.

New social movement theory is concerned with new grievances and collective interests, values and identities.

Postmaterialism refers to value orientation that is concerned with identity and lifestyle rather than with material benefits.

More recently, the distinction between old and new social movements has been less emphasised, noting that supposedly new movements often have precursors in the early twentieth century, and even earlier, while the old movements around material issues have never gone away. Increasingly, all social movements have been seen as examples of contentious politics and theorised in the same framework.

2.2 Resource mobilisation and political process

While the main (West) European contribution to the study of social movements (of which the environmental movement is usually held to be the most prominent example) – the NSM approach – is primarily concerned with the cultural–ideological aspect of collective action, approaches developed in North America focused on movements' resources and opportunities for mobilisation. Here we would like to draw your attention to two kinds of explanation that have proved to be especially influential: one relies for the explanation of the movements' rise and

The **resource mobilisation approach** to social movements emphasises the importance of organisational resources such as skilled organisers, money and knowledge.

Political process models explain social movements by external conditions and in particular by external political opportunities for their mobilisation.

success primarily on its internal resources – the **resource mobilisation approach** (RMA); the other emphasises the importance of external opportunities for mobilisation – the **political process model** (PPM).

The RMA focuses on a movement's ability to mobilise resources, such as money, information or contacts, to promote its campaigns. This may depend on whether the movements are insiders (polity members) or challengers (fighting from the outside). There is also a particular focus on activists as proactive agents in mobilising larger groups of citizens in order to transform or reform a particular structure (such as the economy, state or even social institutions, for example, the cultural influence of a particular religion) and/or seek a more just distribution of costs and benefits in a particular society. The approach began by considering tangible resources and has moved on to include resources which are diverse and not always easily visible.

RMA initially tended to focus on motivations as purely rational cost–benefit calculations and, indeed, some early versions concentrated exclusively on economic causes to explain action (and grappled with the question of why rational individuals would take part in a collective action when they can benefit from the efforts of others as free-riders). The new version of RMA developed by researchers such as Charles Tilly (1994) shifted away from individualistic rational choice to place a greater emphasis on the role of 'political struggle' in framing environmental and other kinds of movements. Tilly also developed the WUNC criteria for measuring success:

- Worthiness – refers to the reputation of the group, often enhanced by the presence of well-respected political actors such as religious leaders, power-holders and people with moral authority (such as Gandhi or Mandela)
- Unity – demonstrated by discipline and collective actions such as demonstrations to affirm a common identity and sense of purpose
- Numbers – indicated by the capacity and willingness to fill a public space, securing mass membership, drawing different sectors of society together or acts such as mass petitions or raising exceptional levels of financial support (for example, internet donations)
- Commitment – demonstrated by activities that carry the risk of harm such as facing off the military and police or willingness to endure legal penalties, as a measure of perseverance.

(Adapted from Tilly, 1994, pp. 1–30)

Each movement has respective strengths and weaknesses in terms of these criteria. For example, a worthy environmental movement (that is one led by people who command a high degree of respect within a society) may be more effective than a movement with a much larger number of members. A movement with a large membership may be less effective than the size would imply due to the erosion of unity by internal divisions. So strengths in one of the criteria can sometimes be accompanied by weaknesses in the others. In some authoritarian situations even strength on all four, such as with the 2007 pro-democracy protests in Burma that linked Buddhist monks, workers, students and wider sections of the population, is no guarantee of success.

Noting that context may count for more than resources, some accounts (for example, McAdam, 1982) highlighted how it is not just the interests and resources of citizens that shape the strategies, internal structure and success of an environmental movement (important as that is), but also the external, changing political context. Initially, he formulated the concept of 'political opportunity structures' that enable or constrain how movements can have an impact on decision making in political institutions. More recently, this has been described in terms of the PPM. Whether a movement or even a more limited campaign on environmental matters has a chance of success depends largely on the willingness and ability of political actors and processes to accommodate their demands and provide arenas within which they can participate and reach accommodations with contending interests, such as those of business or other movements advocating social justice concerns.

Rhetorical strategies can be important both to develop a movement's resources and its ability to influence political processes:

> [a]ctivists tend to present themselves as a solidarity group, preferably as a group with a long history and with coherent existence outside the world of public claim making. Thus feminists identify themselves with women's age-old struggles for rights in the streets and in everyday existence, while environmentalists present most of humankind as their external community.
>
> (Tilly, 2002, p. 89)

Such presentations are not false, but story-telling devices, woven from fragments of fact to unify and embolden a movement. The way that a movement stories itself can have an important effect on its activities and effectiveness.

Doug McAdam et al. (1996) also emphasise the idea of a **cognitive liberation**: that what appeared to be off the agenda and even 'cranky' suddenly becomes politically acceptable and feasible for the first time. Moreover, social relations that were once regarded as 'normal' are reinterpreted as unjust, as shown in Figure 2.2, creating a political space for movements to empower themselves as well as represent their grievances before political authorities. As a result, groups that were

Cognitive liberation refers to the process in which the ideas that were initially politically marginal become politically acceptable.

once excluded as outsiders are increasingly seen as having legitimate concerns. McAdam et al. (1996, p. 6) used this framework to explain the movement for black civil rights in the 1960s in the USA. In fact, this study highlighted how movements that develop a neat fit between their own discourses and those that feature in institutional processes have made 'conscious strategic efforts ... to fashion shared understandings of the world and of themselves that legitimate and motivate collective action'.

Figure 2.2
The foot-soldiers of the black civil rights movement. The Memphis sanitation workers' strike, 1968 (top), the Montgomery bus boycott: arrest of Rosa Parks (bottom)

Environmental movements often find themselves facing opposition from interests that do not want to bear the burdens of environmental regulation or are seeking to push ahead with an environmentally degrading project despite environmental activism against it. These interests are likely to be already embedded in the policy process through political parties and through key actors in the political administration, a particular problem in democratising societies where accountability to citizens is less likely to be firmly established. Use of a discursive 'neat fit' enables environmental actors to do two things. First, addressing environmental concerns in terms of the established meanings and language of the political institutions is essential to preventing these opposed interests from dividing and marginalising the environmental movements involved. Second, it also creates a context for transforming the meanings and language by rearticulating them in ways that make environmental issues central to political discussion. In short, careful attention to political opportunity structures and developing the discourses that maintain what Tilly described as the WUNC formula are essential components of activism and can make the difference between success and failure.

In striving to develop a neat fit between its own discourses and those that feature in institutional processes, social movements perform what Claudia Aradau in Book 1, Chapter 5 called 'speaking with authority'.

However skilful the strategy, movements are likely to have less effectiveness where political repression is more likely and where the goals of these movements contradict the aims of authoritarian regimes, in particularly in societies where the military institutions have substantial economic interests in development projects. For example, in some countries in South East Asia, in the exploitation of timber corrupt patron–client relationships exist that involve the military, so creating barriers for environmental movements where the military have a strong influence on forest policy decisions.

In a series of studies of how the environmental movement has developed in different countries and at different times, Andrew Jamison (2001) has shown how the form and strategies of the movement have differed in different contexts as activists are influenced by different national political styles and cultural preferences. Philip Sarre and Petr Jehlička (2007) have documented how the environmental movement of Czechoslovakia developed through the fall of socialism and separation into Czech and Slovak Republics as political opportunities changed and different resources were mobilised, changing their strategy and rhetoric to pursue their objectives in changing circumstances.

Activity 2.3

Review the discussion of social movements up to this point, and make your own assessment of the relative importance of grievances, identity, resource mobilisation and political process in influencing the effectiveness of the environmental movement organisations you thought about in Activity 2.2.

Without knowing what organisations you are considering, we can't provide specific answers, but we would list the following points as a generalised summary.

- Grievances are rarely decisive, as extreme grievances may exist without movement response, while many activists adopt grievances remote from their everyday life, such as 'save the whales' or the welfare of future generations.
- Identity is important for many NSMs, since it can be the central issue, but less so for the environmental movement, with its worldwide concerns and large membership. Nevertheless, it can play a role in maintaining commitment where local groups face hostility from those against whom they are campaigning.
- Resource mobilisation is important, both in the availability of resources and the skill with which they are used, including use of abstract resources like worthiness.
- Political context is often crucial, both in providing opportunities to exert influence and in selecting what strategies and arguments will be more or less effective.

2.3 From national to international movements

Transnational activist network refers to actors working internationally on an issue, who are bound together by shared values, a common discourse, and dense exchanges of information and services.

The **boomerang effect** refers to the strategy of environmental movements in developing countries to use transnational activist networks to place external pressure on domestic actors.

According to Margaret Keck and Kathryn Sikkink (1998), closed political structures in one country can lead environmental movements to seek transnational and international opportunities to have leverage. **Transnational activist network** refers to actors working internationally on an issue, who are bound together by shared values, a common discourse, and dense exchanges of information and services.

The strategy of using transnational activist networks to place external pressure on domestic political actors and companies, employed by many environmental movements in developing countries, is called the **boomerang effect**.

More genuinely international is the attempt by the environmental movement to influence key policy makers in the international system.

Figure 2.3
A young protester makes a statement against the World Bank in Jakarta, Indonesia, in 2004

The target actors in the environmental context are national governments and international institutions such as the United Nations Environment Programme (UNEP), the World Bank and the World Trade Organization (WTO). Figure 2.3 shows one such protest. Much depends on whether these target actors are vulnerable to environmental actors as a result of prior normative commitments to take account of environmental concerns, a wish to respond to previous damaging criticism from NGOs or possibly because the target actors need to maintain 'good standing' in other international negotiations (Keck and Sikkink, 1998, p. 208). To address global as well as national and local environmental issues, political institutions are constructing new forms of governance, drawing in non-state actors. This creates opportunities for environmental groups to not only influence policy but to shape and implement it as well.

Putting these approaches to environmental movements together by integrating grievances (for no mobilisation occurs without grievance) with the internal dynamics of a movement and with what is often described as the political context external to these movements, means that we can take account of how the latter two influence each other. We can conclude that the way a movement mobilises and its ability to have an impact on state policy, international institutions or, for that matter, on private corporations (that is for-profit private actors) is always context dependent. So, the opportunity structures that exist within political institutions for environmental movements include:

- the capacity of the movement to mobilise support or resources from public opinion and members in order to be taken seriously
- the willingness of political institutions to integrate their concerns
- the willingness and capacity of the state or international agency to initiate measures which address the concerns of the movement.

The meaning of 'capacity' deserves some clarification. Initially the term 'capacity building' in the RMA was focused on developing a coherent and robust network that can articulate a coherent message backed by members of the network. There is a more generalised use of 'capacity building' in the context of the UN and in how political institutions, public–private partnerships, scientific communities and the media can help deliver policy outcomes such as poverty reduction and technological development as well as environmental protection. In the light of the need to integrate a concern with mobilising resources while also taking advantage of opportunity structures in policy making, 'capacity building' can be reinterpreted. In this context, then, **capacity building** involves using whatever resources are on hand to construct accountable procedures for policy formation and implementation that do not exclude those constituencies that are affected by a particular issue (Pangsapa and Smith, 2009). In terms of environmental issues, this will demand not only attempts from outsiders to influence those inside policy communities but also include a concerted and sustained effort by those policy communities to draw in all communities and groups affected by a particular issue so they genuinely feel as if they are stakeholders in the decisions and policies that address this issues. The new key term in this way of understanding capacity is the presence of 'partnerships'. So, as with the meaning of all words, the meaning of 'capacity' has changed depending on the context.

Capacity building involves using resources to construct accountable procedures for policy formation and implementation that do not exclude those constituencies that are affected by a particular issue.

Sidney Tarrow (1998) argued that we need to view political opportunity structures as contingent and fluid, suggesting that movements experience protest cycles whereby they will have phases of influence and involvement where activists can innovate to be better at communicating information to policy makers. Also when considering political opportunity structures in a transnational context, Keck and Sikkink (1998) have highlighted that on the whole, compared to human rights campaigns where rights are more clearly defined and have an embedded legal presence, environmental movements face greater obstacles.

Even though some international institutions may be more susceptible to environmental movements, this reinforces the need for initiatives such as the World Environmental Organisation (WEO), as discussed in the previous chapter.

2.4 Incorporation of the mainstream environmental movement

In a situation where governments and international agencies increasingly stress bringing civil society organisations into governance, successful social movement organisations can face a new danger: as they get closer to government and/or business, they may both find it necessary to compromise their demands and behave more like civil servants or managers. This process is called **incorporation**, and is a danger for mainstream environmental organisations.

Incorporation of environmental groups refers to the process by which they are active participants in consultation on policy formation and implementation. In some cases, this can include partnerships with governments and corporations.

Environmental protection groups have often been characterised as 'narrow-focus environmentalism' (Agyeman and Angus, 2003), since many environmental protection groups tend to view environmental policy as distinct from other issues. Critics also highlight that many environmental NGOs have limited if any internal democratic mechanisms and a narrow membership in social terms (usually up-scale and college educated as well as from specific ethnic groups). Indeed, many NGOs involve activists who are unelected and in some cases self-appointed advocates of the interests of the environment. While this may be expected in organisations that are by definition 'non-governmental' we should also remember that these groups claim to represent a variety of constituencies: environmental NGOs act as advocates for the environment in general, species or particular bioregions. However, in most cases local communities, neighbourhoods or citizens also have an interest in these environments or species, whether it is for their livelihoods or recreational use. As a result, it is arguable that environmental NGOs should be more proactive in developing accountable decision-making processes themselves. This becomes more pressing as NGOs move from being external critics to internal participants in governance.

As Paul Jepson (2005) argued, environmental NGOs now have a dual role. First, they highlight environmental harm and the need for corporate accountability as a result of the declining importance of representative governments, which has 'helped secure the NGO voice at high level policy fora'. Second, many environmental NGOs 'have willingly supported the move to shift public service delivery to civil society ... by lobbying for lucrative contracts to supply data, for example analyses on the state of the environment, or to deliver components of development projects' (Jepson, 2005, p. 516). Referring primarily to the major British NGOs, Jepson defines these 'Green-chip environmental non-governmental organisations (ENGOs)' as a morph between a state development agency and a transnational corporation, which have taken advantage of increased political access to develop new resources beyond membership subscriptions to include public grants, corporate sponsorship and private charitable foundations.

Legitimacy is 'the perception or assumption that the actions of an entity are desirable, proper, or appropriate within some socially constructed system of norms, values, beliefs, and definitions'.

This generates a number of concerns for environmental activists whose credibility depends on their **legitimacy**. According to Mark Suchman (1995, p. 574), legitimacy is 'the perception or assumption that the actions of an entity are desirable, proper, or appropriate within some socially constructed system of norms, values, beliefs, and definitions'. NGOS are said to be legitimate when their members, donors and supporters regard their practices as beneficial and appropriate. Environmental NGOs have concerns about whether state regulation of NGO accountability will provide a rigid framework unsuited to their organisation and are also worried about the corporate practices of performance targets and audits being applied. As Jepson (2005, p. 517) argues, as companies increasingly adopt corporate social responsibility (CSR) platforms, in strategic partnerships with NGOs, 'many corporations now expect a major ENGO to meet similar governance and accountability standards to their own'.

Corporate social responsibility was discussed in Book 2, Chapter 10

Interestingly, Jepson's research with NGO leaders highlights a key concern that even discussing accountability will open them up to attacks from 'anti-environmentalists' and that this in turn will affect their capacity to secure membership subscriptions and donations. Nevertheless, some environmental NGOs are beginning to address this by developing horizontal (as opposed to hierarchical) organisations that make the NGO more responsive to local concerns (for example, the Woodland Trust and Friends of the Earth in the British context), de-linking the membership magazine from the executive body of the NGO so that different views and wider debates are covered in, for example, magazine publications (Campaign to Protect Rural England's *Countryside Voice*), and devising new ways of consulting with their supporter base such as creating 'membership services department' to answer members' questions (Royal Society for the Protection of Birds) as well as questionnaires and focus groups. However, major NGOs remain complex organisations as shown in Figure 2.4.

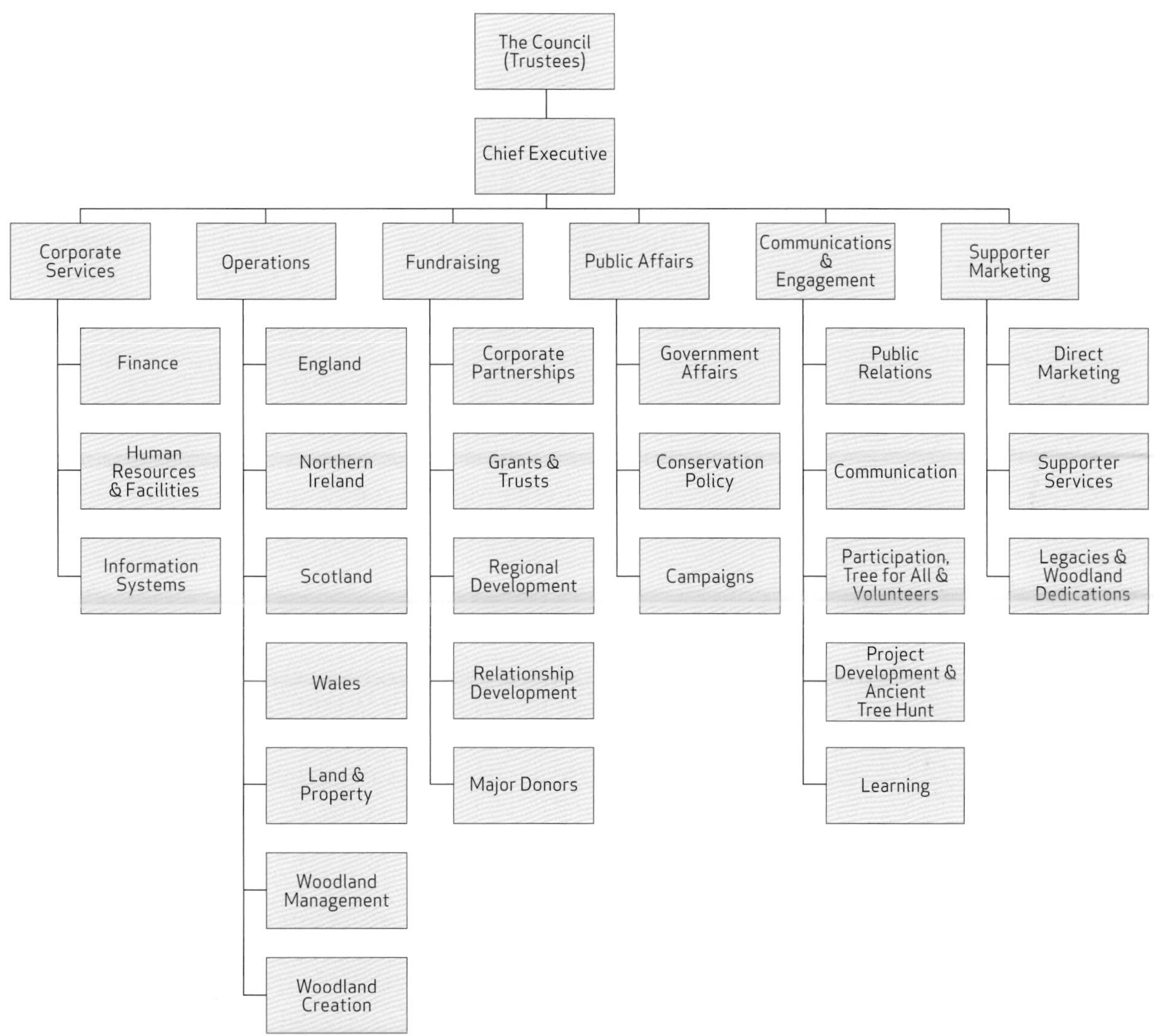

Figure 2.4
The organisational structure of the Woodland Trust

With the development of partnership arrangements, a key issue is that these NGOs become larger and increasingly tied to public service delivery and government agendas. Rather than seeking and advocating social change, they have often adopted the role of scientific and policy innovators in a number of institutionalised settings (Diani and Rambaldo, 2007). The objectives of partners such as companies donating funding is likely to prioritise less controversial activities and middle-class concerns, such as nature preservation and the promotion of green consumerism, and marginalise more radical issues, such as the storage and disposal of hazardous waste, addressing poverty and social deprivation, and providing the resources to improve the quality of life of underprivileged groups.

Nature preservation was introduced in Book 2, Chapter 5

Green consumerism will be discussed in Chapter 4 of this book

Activity 2.4

Select an environmental organisation or movement with which you are familiar, or of which you are a member, as your case study. Complete research on the governance structure of your selected case. Some of this research may need to be completed online, especially if you do not have ready access to the organisation's publicity materials. Now complete the following tasks and questions.

1 Clearly identify the goals of your selected case.

2 Summarise the range of activities of your selected case.

3 To what extent is your selected case involved in partnerships with political institutions and other NGOs such as companies and private charities as well as other movement organisations?

4 What steps has your selected case taken to ensure accountability to its membership?

5 Do you find any indications that your case has lost its critical edge as a result of incorporation?

Assuming that you would be most likely to choose large, well-known organisations, we expect that you would have concluded that they were moderate in their demands, close to decision makers and often involved in activities funded by business or government. However, you may have chosen groups, such as roads protest groups or well-known

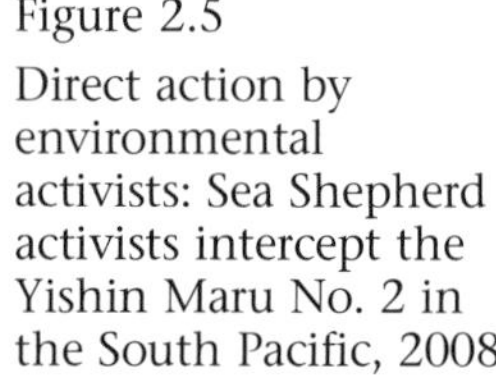

Figure 2.5
Direct action by environmental activists: Sea Shepherd activists intercept the Yishin Maru No. 2 in the South Pacific, 2008

organisations such as Earth First! or Sea Shepherd, that remain outsiders and oppositional, often choosing to confront activities they regard as harmful, as shown in Figure 2.5. These are an indication that there is plenty of activity outside what we have called 'the mainstream', a point emphasised in the next section, where we will assess the applicability of the concepts from social movement theory, including the RMA and the PPM, to the Environmental Justice Movement (EJM), which is based in North America. As stated at the beginning of this section, while in the past often marginalised in both academic and political discussions, the EJM has recently inspired environmental movements all over the world.

3 The Environmental Justice Movement

This section examines the emergence of the EJM in the USA, with its explicit attempt to address the link between environmental hazards and the social composition of the groups most affected by them. In historical terms, the EJM is said to have emerged as an oppositional movement in a poor African American community in Warren County, North Carolina, when state authorities wanted to dispose of waste contaminated with polychlorinated biphenyls (PCBs) in local landfills, resulting in over 500 arrests of residents in the autumn of 1982, as shown in Figure 2.6.

Figure 2.6
Direct action for environmental justice: Warren County protesters line the highway in an attempt to block trucks loaded with PCB tainted dirt in 1982

3.1 Social marginalisation and environmental inequity

The core claim of the EJM focuses on environmental justice, based on the grievance that risk of environmental harm is unequally distributed across citizens and specific locations. However, for Julian Agyeman (2002), who in 1988 co-founded the Black Environment Network in the UK, as well as for key EJM advocates such as Robert Bullard (1990), today environmental justice goes beyond identifying those who bear more of the environmental costs and fewer environmental benefits; it also addresses who is consulted in participatory processes. This means looking beyond differences based on ethnicity to accepting that white working-class people also often suffer from injustices of this kind – highlighting how environmental injustice tends to penalise 'the marginalised', rather than any specific group in all contexts (as occurs with some generalised notions of the working class).

This movement emerged from a concern with the production, storage and disposal of hazardous waste in neighbourhoods with low socio-economic status and weak civic engagement. Recognising that their interests have been harmed and that their voices have not been heard this movement has been predominantly driven from the grassroots by local communities, later spreading to farm workers' unions, anti-toxics movements and Hispanic and Native American struggles for self-determination. The experience of the affected communities led to considerable empowerment as well as opportunities to link their concerns to those of the black civil rights movement, women's groups and academic researchers.

Bullard (1987) showed how black middle-class communities in Northwood Manor (Houston, Texas) realised they had common cause with poorer communities. In this case, garbage facilities were located in suburban residential neighbourhoods that were 82 per cent African-American. In a chilling anticipation of the experience of the clean-up after Hurricane Katrina in New Orleans in 2005, Bullard highlighted how the debris from the 1983 Hurricane Alicia was dumped and burnt in the poor black community in Bordersville with all its attendant health consequences. His subsequent work extended the analysis of Houston to other states such as West Virginia, Louisiana and Alabama and then covered African- and Hispanic-American communities in cities like Los Angeles, where similar protest movements against environmental hazards had emerged.

Environmental injustices that occurred in New Orleans in the aftermath of the 2005 Hurricane Katrina were discussed in Book 2, Chapter 3

Dumping in Dixie, Bullard's (1990) landmark study of environmental hazards and racial discrimination in the USA, identified how noxious production facilities and the distribution of 'toxics' (such as PCBs and dioxins) tended to be located in the path of least resistance, that is in the neighbourhoods of the poor and the powerless. Perhaps one of the reasons for the considerable mobilisation of resources was the racial segregation of many US cities, which means that in many cases affluent, middle-class and working-class black communities have close proximity, so that people with more resources identified with the grievances of the poor. Racial segregation also made it possible to link their protests against environmental injustice to equal rights legislation that forbade racially discriminatory outcomes, and hence gave them a powerful weapon to use in the courts.

From the start, the EJM drew extensively on women's support, as described by Rachel Stein:

> Women are often the caretakers, the daily observers who are the first to notice what is amiss in the family, community, and local environment; so it is often female relatives or caregivers who mobilize in order to protect children and other loved ones from ills such as asthma or lead poisoning that are aggravated by environmental factors. These women challenge political leaders and health experts who ignore or belittle their suffering while blaming mothers for poor care.
>
> (Stein, 2004, p. 11)

In most cases of the EJM, unlike many environmental campaigns, the movements were able to depend on the resources, networking capabilities and passions of all generations of the affected communities, both women and men, and while the hazards predominantly impacted on the poor and powerless, the movements drew members from across social classes. Dorceta Taylor (2000) argues that the flourishing of the EJM as an oppositional movement, pressuring from the outside but often with little effect, coincided with the irresponsiveness of the Reagan–Bush administrations of 1981–93 while the Clinton administration 1993–2001 incorporated environmental justice activists and Congress was receptive to EJM concerns (just as Theodore Roosevelt's tenure as president was receptive to both conservationist and preservationist concerns in the early twentieth century with the establishment of the national park system). In addition, she highlights how the EJM mobilised scientific support, policy activism and the coordination of local campaigns in broader movements for change.

The distinction between conservation and preservation was drawn in Book 2, Chapter 5

These movements secured concessions from the state for regulatory oversight by achieving an Office for Environmental Justice in the EPA as well as the establishment of the National Environmental Justice Advisory Council (NEJAC). This brought together EPA officials with academic researchers, industrialists, political leaders (including indigenous Americans) and community organisations to develop a common dialogue on integrating environmental justice in all aspects of its work. This marked a shift in group organisation: from mobilising resources to taking more explicit advantages of the opportunities for influencing decision making in existing political structures. However, the George W. Bush administration of 2001–09 has closed off many opportunities for the movement at federal level and as a result activists have focused more on initiatives at a local and state level, which had historically always served them well.

Online Exercise 15

Now log on to the course website and complete Online Exercise 15: *Researching the environmental justice movement.*

3.2 Comparing environmental protection and environmental justice movements

Activity 2.5

Drawing on information on environmental protection movements in this chapter and elsewhere in the course, consider how groups and organisations focused on environmental justice and on environmental protection differ. Make notes accordingly.

If you chose North American movements as an example, you are likely to have identified considerable differences between how environmental issues are understood by groups such as the Sierra Club or the US branch of Friends of the Earth and the EJM. For example, the Sierra Club has a key focus on the protection of wild places and the protection of ecosystems that have so far been relatively unaffected by human impacts, in the traditions of John Muir's environmental philosophy. As a result, even when considering questions of environmental justice, the Sierra Club is often concerned with preserving pristine environments rather than addressing the complex issues of urban environments head on, unless they are also affected by the degradation of those environments. On the other hand, the EJM was from the start concerned with environments that are largely not pristine. As a result, its focus has been on toxic waste, waste storage and local sources of air and water pollution that have a disproportionate effect on certain segments of the population.

There are also usually considerable differences in the social composition of the membership and associated resources of the movements, groups and NGOs in question. The demographic evidence on environmental protection movements suggests that members and, especially importantly, activists tend to be drawn disproportionately from more highly educated and higher-income segments of the population in North America. This is especially the case with national organisations such as the Sierra Club and the National Audubon Society. According to Thomas Burns and Terri LeMoyne (2001), this contrast becomes even more marked when comparing these 'eco-establishment' NGOs (Seager, 1993) with the localised, grassroots, urban-based and developing society environmental movements, which typically have more diverse memberships and are more likely to include lower paid, minority and working-class activists. While there is little evidence of a gender divide in environmental protection movements in terms of membership, there is a preponderance of men in senior positions in most major organisations.

3.3 Towards 'co-activism' and 'just sustainability'

In spite of the EJM's fundamental differences from the mainstream groups, since the mid 1990s the EJM also began developing its own institutional experiments as it became more focused on the political process and working with the opportunities in US political institutions. In the context of the gains made by minorities through civil rights legislation within the legal system, the EJM couched its demands and rhetoric in terms of a previously successful discourse of civil rights, linking environmental questions to ones of equity between groups constructed in 'racial' terms. However, rather than depending on mainstream political institutions, the EJM also drew in a variety of institutions that were regarded as civil organisations such as charities and church groups as well as groups such as the National Association for the Advancement of Colored People (NAACP, the oldest civil rights organisation in the USA, set up in 1909) that explicitly engage in the traditional interface of state and civil society.

However, according to Agyeman and Briony Angus (2003), the EJM now does something more than this by attempting to link social and environmental issues through what they describe as 'broad-focus civic environmentalism' – which explicitly links the RMA and the PPM. In this account, issues as diverse as civic disengagement, racial and class-based segregation, urban disinvestment, high crime rates and unemployment are seen as intimately linked to environmental degradation. The goals of justice expressed by union campaigns and community activism are no longer seen as incompatible with those of environmentalists. Active citizenship focuses on our obligations to foster the combined social, environmental and economic health of communities, while recognising that procedural processes (such as deliberative democracy, consensus conferencing and so on) are important, at the same time acknowledging that they should not be separated from substantive goals and outcomes.

Deliberative democracy was introduced in Book 1, Chapter 6

Public–private partnership was introduced in Book 2, Chapter 5

Thus, while the EJM shifted its focus to institutional lobbying and developing public–private partnerships and has become a participant in environmental governance, it has also, through civil rights discourse, articulated grievances and outlined a standpoint based on environmental rights which goes beyond the concerns of traditional environmental NGOs. In turn this has provided a degree of legitimacy that is often very hard to achieve for oppositional movements. Within environmental movements, there are already significant attempts to bridge the gap between backyard or grassroots local environmental justice campaigns and NGOs concerned with sustainability. For some, this points the way to a more effective co-activism, involving some kind of movement fusion so that the policies proposed are more than a shopping list of different policies on different issues between partners of a coalition; the base of support of both partners expands (Cole and Foster, 2001).

Co-activism means that each policy should address all the different constituencies as part of a coordinated campaign.

Co-activism means that each policy should address all the different constituencies as part of a coordinated campaign. One example is the campaign on 'just transportation' (Bullard and Johnson, 1997; Conservation Law Foundation, 1998), which sought to address the obstacles and barriers that inhibited the ability of some racial and class groups from having adequate mobility. The point was not to increase the amount of car pollution and the level of congestion by ensuring that all citizens could freely drive SUVs. It does mean that within the scope of defined limits on car pollution, we should ensure that all citizens have adequate experience of environmental goods (such as access to green spaces). It also means that highway construction, which benefits the economically secure members of a society (particularly multiple-car households), does not take place in a way that inflicts higher levels of car pollution and its health effects on those citizens least able to own their own means of private transportation.

To illustrate, not only does the inner-city urban population tend to experience a disproportionate impact from pollution such as toxic waste, but spending on transport is often higher in the suburbs than in minority and low-income neighbourhoods. It is often the case in affluent societies that the areas with the highest air pollution levels resulting from car use coincide with the lowest car ownership. This reminds us that in many environmental matters, as John Westergaard and Henrietta Resler (1976) stated, *power is visible in its consequences*. So, if a socially and politically marginalised community experiences most of the environmental 'bads' and few environmental 'goods', then even if it is hard to provide causal attribution, then power has been exercised even if no decisions can be pinpointed as a direct cause.

The conclusion that we can draw from these examples of broad focus civic environmentalism is that environmental injustice should not be seen as a simple result of a lack of access to environmental goods (and avoidance of bads), but as a result of the inability of communities to be responsible for and develop active strategies that promote economic vitality, ecological integrity, civic democracy and social well-being. This is now increasingly described as a **just sustainability** (Agyeman, 2005; Agyeman et al., 2003) that involves practical solutions that simultaneously address social and environmental justice. This movement is thus not just concerned about dumping or the development of LULUs ('locally unwanted land uses', such as waste transfer facilities), it is also concerned about creating access to environmental quality – increasing access to goods such as the countryside and urban green spaces.

Just sustainability involves practical solutions that simultaneously address social and environmental justice and is concerned with both preventing 'bads' ending up in marginalised communities and getting access to environmental 'goods'.

The concept of LULUs was introduced in Book 1, Chapter 5

The language and tactics of the US EJM have been taken up both by groups in other countries and by organisations campaigning against the international financial institutions and even in negotiations on climate change, where the concept of climate justice points out that the sufferers from climate change are often the poor, who have contributed very little to levels of greenhouse gases. Schlosberg (2007, pp. 45–78) discusses the wider EJM, pointing out that they now claim recognition and participation as well as more even distribution of environmental goods and bads. Although the basic claim for justice may be similar, activists have to use different strategies and language, because the political context is always different. For example, as considered in Section 4, in Asia it is expressed through, for example, the Buddhist understanding of suffering and balance. Each context is already occupied by discourses that regulate the production of meaning, and we need to recognise the crucial role they play in environmental communication and mobilisation.

4 Environmental activism in Asia

So far this chapter has considered theories and case studies from Europe and North America, so to broaden the scope of the analysis developed above, we focus in this section on some examples of environmental movements in Asia, namely in Thailand and China. Rapid industrialisation in Asia has created a wide variety of environmental problems as it has become the workshop of the world. The problems of deforestation are particularly acute on the South East Asian mainland and Indonesian archipelago. Air pollution has increased dramatically in special economic zones in countries such as China and Thailand, as was evident in the air quality difficulties in the lead-up to the 2008 Beijing Olympics. But although grievances are serious, activism has been limited because political opportunities and resources are more limited than in democratic, high-income countries.

4.1 The Chinese environmental movement: working within the state-determined opportunity structure

The factory and energy production processes used in the past in the industrialisation of developed countries included many chemicals and other industrial products that are now banned in these contexts. However, they are still widely used in developing countries, for example, lead in paint in China and hazardous leather softeners in India. In addition, the regulatory frameworks that protect consumers, workers, communities and the environment in developed countries are either absent or sometimes ignored in developing countries. Only since 2000 have the effects of such rapid development and industrialisation become the focus of attention. Elizabeth Economy, writing in *The River Runs Black* (2004) on China and the wider Asia Pacific region, captures this especially well when she states that:

> [t]his rapid development also produced an environmental disaster that was largely ignored in the planning calculus of the region's leaders. Like the countries of Eastern Europe and the former Soviet republics, the Asia Pacific region as a whole suffered from disregard for environmental protection, weak environmental protection institutions, and little opportunity for public participation. Moreover, like China, the Asia Pacific region also suffers the environmental burdens of growing automobile use, urbanization, and migration among other concerns.
>
> (Economy, 2004, p. 236)

Environmental and social consequences of rapid industrialisation in India were discussed in depth in Book 2, Chapter 2

According to Economy, the main problem in China is water-borne pollutants because of the effects of untreated waste from factories, agriculture and households in the waterways. It is hard to comprehend the extent of the transformation of China since the 1990s, but the growing factory zones (such as the Pearl River delta) have caused huge social and demographic upheavals within China itself, where internal migration is the most intense in the world. The pressure on land use to provide food for growing and more affluent urban populations has increased and, combined with fewer sources of uncontaminated water, has generated considerable desertification in the Chinese inland regions. This in turn contributes to the deteriorating air quality of Chinese cities as a result of dust storms. Rapid development has also contributed to greenhouse gas emissions. China's cement production was projected to double between 2005 and 2015, while coal production doubled between 2000 and 2004 and was expected to increase by a further billion tonnes by 2010, with all its associated effects in terms of sulphur dioxide (SO_2) emissions and the problems of acid rain for China itself, but also South Korea and Japan.

Figure 2.7
The urban landscape saturated with cars in China. Beijing, August 2007 (left), Xiamen, Fujian Province, January 2007 (right)

Local environmental effects of rapid industrialisation generate deeply felt grievances. For example, in 2001 at the Jing Quan rice-wine factory in north-east China, the hydrofluoric acid used to etch bottles (incidentally with only the protection of rubber gloves) was disposed of in an unlined pit that contaminated local water supplies in Leifeng and Puxing, causing deaths in livestock, skin rashes, stomach disorders and, according to reports (McLaughlin, 2006; Smith and Pangsapa, 2008, pp. 125–6), making at least 500 people seriously ill. The China Centre for Legal Assistance to Pollution Victims, an NGO specialising in legal advocacy though in the context of limited environmental law, has initiated legal cases with mixed success. It identifies a number of key problems: there is little evidence of systematic use of **environmental impact assessment (EIA)** (analysis of the environmental consequences of projects and policies) and dangerous production processes have been placed in high-population areas and close to waterways while pollution control technologies are often absent. When regulations are applied, usually only in response to severe environmental harm and the threat of social unrest, as Economy (2004) documents, the factories usually relocate and resume operations on the same terms. Alternatively, where waste treatment facilities are introduced as a result of state action, the costs can lead factory owners to switch them off when the coast is clear. As a result, waste disposal is often in its pure form or merely diluted by water: the public lacked awareness about the problems until it generated widespread illness.

Environmental impact assessment (EIA) is an analytical process that examines environmental consequences of projects and policies and provides accounts of alternative courses of actions prior to their implementation.

While environmental protection bureaus exist in each locality, pressures from political and business sources mean that they are reluctant to enforce regulations. As a result of this lax regulatory system, reporting by factories only occurs in seriously polluting industries and environmental information is scarce (Wang and Xu, 2007). Most importantly, the Chinese legal system lacks clear compensation standards for the harms caused by pollution and, if legal cases emerge, only some judges have environmental law training. Causal attribution is much easier to establish on water-borne pollution and explain in a legal context while air pollution is much more difficult (Alford and Liebman, 2001; Smith and Pangsapa, 2008; Turner and Hildebrandt, 2002; Wang and Ongley, 2004). In this context, political opportunity is limited as a result of undemocratic political institutions and the close links of state officials to the business sector. As indicated above, NGOs do operate, but within narrow constraints and with limited influence.

While the EJM seized on the political opportunity offered by the discourse of civil rights, here environmental movements drew on the discourse of Confucian philosophy, now actively promoted by the Chinese ruling Communist party. The emphasis in this is less on rights and more on understanding rites, couched in terms of responsibility to the broader social context and implied acceptance of established political authority. In opposition to self-interest and individualism, Confucianism has clear boundaries between how we pursue our own interests and how we affect others. In terms of the environment, Confucian ideas place a great emphasis on respect for nature as part of 'a unity of heaven and humanity' (*tianrenheyi*). It starts from the premise of interdependency between society and nature. Confucian assumptions offer a greater emphasis on duties and obligations and so lend themselves more readily to developing a discourse of environmental responsibility. However, fostering a greater respect for nature and promoting the virtues of sincerity, benevolence, filial piety and propriety (through which the practice of goodness could be cultivated) is inhibited by the government's focus on material growth and development (Stimpson, 2000).

Since local resource mobilisation is difficult domestically, environmental activists organised in loose networks and often acting individually (such as Wu Song at Shantou University [Johnson, 2006]) looked for transnational resources and opportunity structures. A useful example is the Basel Action Network (BAN), a network developed by Earth Economics (an environmental NGO based in Washington state in the USA), which has highlighted the growing trade in e-waste, with 80 per cent going to developing countries in Asia and most of this to China, as shown in Figure 2.8. The BAN was founded after the 1989 Basel Convention on the movement and disposal of transboundary waste, which came into force in 1992. It was amended in 1994 to secure a ban on the disposal of toxic waste in developing countries, which it sees as an act of environmental injustice that is tantamount to both environmental crime and a human rights violation. The main obstacle to progress is that the USA (the main exporter of computer and other electronic waste) not only failed to ratify the Basel Convention but its regulatory agency, the EPA, only started to monitor and seek restrictions on e-waste exports in the middle of the first decade of the twenty-first century. In 2006 the EPA agreed to require 'prior confirmed consent' for exports of cathode ray tubes but, according to BAN, this has not been enforced. In the absence of a response from either

The Basel Convention and the international hazardous waste trade were discussed in Book 2, Chapter 7

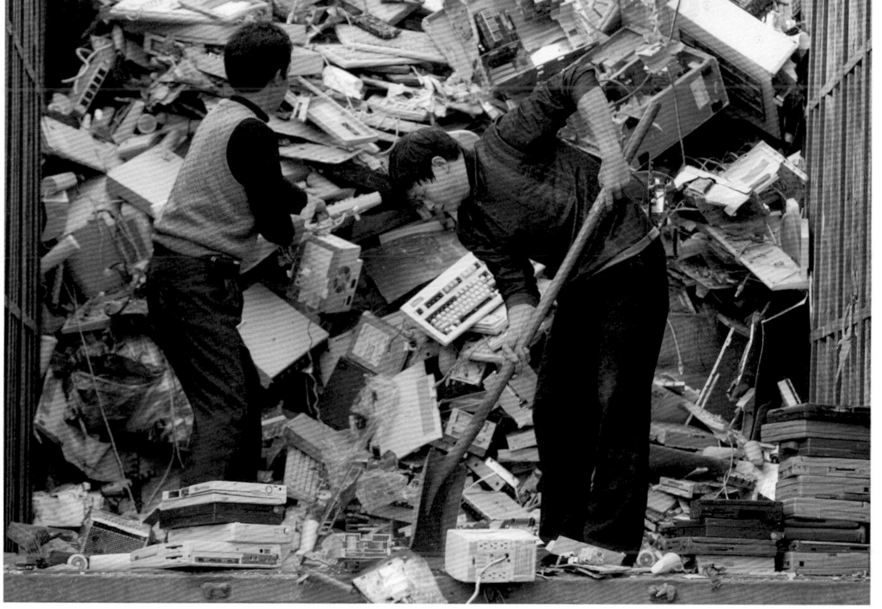

Figure 2.8
E-waste exported by the West to China

of the main governments concerned, even the link to international networks has had little impact on the effectiveness of Chinese environmentalists.

4.2 The Thai environmental movement: from elite incorporation to grassroots protest

Unlike China, environmental groups in some Asian societies have played a more important role in the generation of environmental concerns. It should be stressed, however, that in many of these political regimes, the political opportunity structures are still much more limited than in the case of European and North American environmental protection movements and EJM in the USA. In Thailand, state consultation on environmental policy is limited to state agencies and established NGOs (such as the Thai Environment Institute [TEI]), drawing from 'respected' scientists and the urban elite, so adding few new perspectives (Hirsch, 1997; Smith and Pangsapa, 2008). Western influenced organisations devoted to environmental protection tended to adopt the view that best answers were to be discovered through the use of scientific expertise and through external consultants hired to promote development while minimising environmental effects (Hirsch, 1997; Lang, 2003; Maneepong, 2006; Pfirrman and Kron, 1992). This is

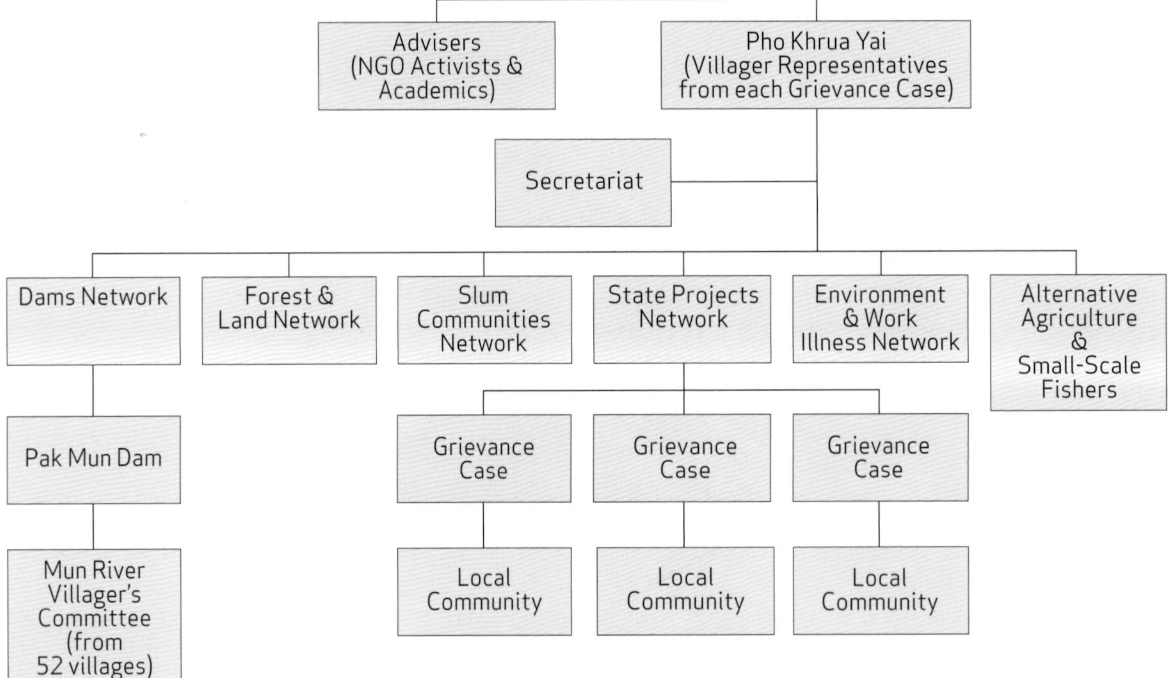

Figure 2.9
Internal structure of the Assembly of the Poor in Thailand

compounded by a patronising attitude to rural Thais as uneducated and uncultured, hence the media descriptions of protesters as the 'people of the fermented fish'. Nevertheless, there are oppositional movements generating significant embarrassment for the political authorities, taking advantage of Thailand's lively news media. In Thailand during the 1990s and under Thaksin Shinawatra's democratising administration between 2001 and 2006, a broad-based movement, the Assembly of the Poor (see Figure 2.9), emerged as a serious challenge to government policies on natural resource use, land rights, community livelihoods and a range of other issues such as working conditions (pressed by the Council of Work and Environment Related Patients' Network [WEPT]) and the environmental damage caused by tourism (Baker, 2000; Missingham, 2003a and 2003b; Sivaraksa, 2002).

The core of the movement was formed by the communities displaced and adversely affected by development projects such as the Pak Mun dam (which included not simply submersion of land but biodiversity loss in the fisheries both up- and downstream). The Assembly of the Poor developed into a broad coalition of NGOs and movements which sought to use a variety of tactics to raise the profile of these issues, including media-savvy tactics to generate increased television and press coverage (as illustrated in Figure 2.10). What is distinctive about this movement is that it had a grassroots membership and explicitly linked social and environmental issues. Although seen as lacking 'worthiness', it unified significant numbers, many of whom were committed to take action, since they had little left to lose.

The Assembly of the Poor was established to defend the economic interests of its member organisations. However, in the context of a Buddhist society, these interests included an integral relationship with the environments that supported their livelihoods or which had been damaged by development projects. These development projects included hydroelectric power plants, coal-fired power plants or the effects of deforestation that followed the growth of eucalyptus and bamboo to provide supposedly eco-friendly paper in the USA. This movement drew upon the resources of members that were for the most part poorly educated as well as poor in economic terms. In addition, the Assembly of the Poor also drew in some of the urban elite environmental campaigners and NGO representatives that had previously ignored these concerns.

There are good reasons why this mobilisation came about. Thailand had a historic problem with providing water resources for agriculture (a key element of the national programme for growth in the first place) as well as more recently in generating sufficient energy sources to cope with the rapid industrialisation of the country. As a result, most river systems

Figure 2.10
Assembling the poor: media-oriented protests in Bangkok, 2003

that could serve as hydroelectric power resources had been affected and there were limited alternative fuel resources in the country. At the same time, the environmental and community livelihood movements that had emerged to mitigate the effects of these projects had managed to successfully pressurise the government to offer compensation to some of the affected communities, but also open to the sluice gates of dams such as Pak Mun to allow better access to water downstream and facilitate the migration of fish species for spawning that had hitherto been part of the local economy (Pangsapa and Smith, 2008).

One of the distinctive qualities of environmental movements is their capacity to bring in local knowledges in ways that do not always correspond to the accounts developed by outside experts, an issue discussed in the next chapter. In the case of the Assembly of the Poor, community campaigns have drawn upon local knowledge through participatory research. This involves local community members collecting empirical data for researchers based on their detailed acquired knowledge of their own environments. For example, after the completion of the Pak Mun dam, research was conducted by residents of local villagers to identify the extent of biodiversity loss in the fisheries. In addition, the community researchers were able to draw on local multigenerational knowledge (comparing their results with elder members of the communities who could specify historic fisheries). It also led many participants to highlight the difference between traditional methods of resource management and the accounts developed by development project companies and state officials (Ganjanapan, 2000; Ganjanapan, 1997; GCM, 2005; Hirsch, 1998; Laungaramsri, 2002).

Activity 2.6

Using Table 2.1, compare and consider the cases in this section and make notes accordingly.

Table 2.1 Comparing and analysing environmental activism in Asia

Countries	China	Thailand
Key environmental issues raised		
Political context as constraint or enabler for environmental action		
Role of environmental NGOs		
What is revealed by applying the RMA to this example?		
What is revealed by applying the PPM approach to this example?		

Our brief summary would be to say that, though the grievances in both countries are similar, stemming from prioritisation of rapid economic growth, the political opportunities are significantly different, with China still a one-party state and Thailand moving towards democracy. Hence, in China mobilisation has involved attempts to use the law internally and to connect with overseas allies, but in both cases has been stifled by the state. In Thailand formal political rights and access to a freer media have allowed some mobilisation, even by the poor. Connecting environmental and livelihood issues, and bringing together large numbers of people have been effective strategies.

5 Conclusion

In the last two chapters you've encountered a range of environmental issues and cases of environmental action. According to Michael Edwards (2001, p. 2), 'the rights and responsibilities of citizenship at a global level are ill defined' and complicated by the democratic deficit in existing arrangements for global governance as well as in many democratising countries. Nevertheless, despite these obstacles, as you've worked through this chapter, you will have seen that environmental actors even at the grassroots level are increasingly linking local activities to similar activities in other countries and developing networks that are transnational in character. As a result, environmental NGOs are beginning to change both their internal structures and their activities. They are beginning to develop new ways to be accountable to their members and develop stronger links with grassroots movements. They are also reaching out to other NGOs and movements that cover related environmental and developmental issues in order to exchange knowledge and build co-activist strategies that address the concerns of both partners, but in a more effective way. Here we want to highlight two issues: the insights stemming from the application of social movement theory and the significance of using justice claims to link social and environmental issues.

As regards the theories, the main insight is that movement effectiveness may be as strongly influenced by the context in which it is working as by its skill in building and mobilising the resources it commands. In democratic countries, the political opportunities are much wider, though paradoxically success in being accepted as political insiders may have reduced movement radicalism. In developing societies such as China and Thailand, where resource mobilisation is seen as a threat to political institutions and where the political opportunity structure is more limited than in Western contexts, two options seem available. As you've seen, one way of compensating for the limited opportunities experienced by environmental movements in developing countries is to draw on opportunities arising from transnational networking and on the resources of foreign or international NGOs to place pressure on national governments and private corporations to develop practices and partnerships that embrace environmental responsibility. Another way is the creative adapting of the grievances of environmental movements to the political discourses that operate in political institutions whether that be Confucianism in China or Buddhism in Thailand. As the adaptation of the civil rights discourse by the US EJM showed, less well-resourced movements in affluent democracies sometimes have to follow similar strategies.

Video 5

Now watch Video 5: *Unequal relations in international negotiations.*

References

Agyeman, J. (2002) 'Constructing environmental (in)justice: transatlantic tales', *Environmental Politics*, vol. 11, no. 3, pp. 31–5.

Agyeman, J. (2005) *Sustainable Communities and the Challenge of Environmental Justice*, New York, New York University Press.

Agyeman, J. and Angus, B. (2003) 'The role of civic environmentalism in the pursuit of sustainable communities', *Journal of Urban and Environmental Policy and Planning*, vol. 46, pp. 345–63.

Agyeman, J., Bullard, R. D. and Evans, B. (eds) (2003) *Just Sustainabilities: Development in an Unequal World*, London, Earthscan.

Alford, W. P. and Liebman, B. L. (2001) 'Clean air, clear processes? The struggle over air pollution in the People's Republic of China', *Hastings Law Journal*, vol. 52, no. 3, pp. 703–37.

Baker, C. (2000) 'Thailand's Assembly of the Poor: background, drama, reaction', *South East Asia Research*, vol. 8, no. 1, pp. 5–29.

Bullard, R. D. (1987) *Invisible Houston: the Black Experience in Boom and Bust*, College Station, TX, Texas A&M University Press.

Bullard, R. D. (1990) *Dumping in Dixie: Race, Class and Environmental Quality*, Boulder, CO, Westview Press.

Bullard, R. D. and Johnson, S. (1997) *Just Transportation*, Gabriola Island, BC, Island Press.

Burns, T. J. and LeMoyne, T. (2001) 'How environmental movements can be more effective: prioritizing environmental themes in political discourse', *Human Ecology Review*, vol. 8, no. 1, pp. 26–38.

Carmin, J. (1999) 'Voluntary associations, professional organizations, and the environmental movement in the United States', *Environmental Politics*, vol. 8, no. XY, pp. 101–21.

Cole, L. W. and Foster, S. R. (2001) *From the Ground Up: Environmental Racism and the Rise of the Environmental Justice Movement*, New York, New York University Press.

Conservation Law Foundation (1998) *City Routes, City Right: Building Liveable Neighborhoods and Environmental Justice by Fixing Transportation*, Boston, MA, Conservation Law Foundation.

Diani, M. and Rambaldo, E. (2007) 'Still the time of environmental movements? A local perspective', *Environmental Politics*, vol. 16, no. 5, pp. 765–84.

Economy, E. C. (2004) *The River Runs Black: The Environmental Challenge to China's Future*, Ithaca, NY, Cornell University Press.

Edwards, M. (2001) 'Introduction' in Edwards, M. and Gaventa, J. (eds) *Global Citizen Action*, Boulder, CO, Lynne Rienner Publishers.

Ganjanapan, A. (2000) *Local Control of Land and Forest: Cultural Dimensions of Resource Management in Northern Thailand*, Chiang Mai, Regional Centre for Social Science and Sustainable Development, Chiang Mai University.

Ganjanapan, S. (1997) 'Indigenous and scientific concepts of forest and land classification in northern Thailand' in Hirsch, P. (ed.) (1997).

Global Community Monitor (GCM) (2005) 'Thailand's air: poison cocktail – exposing unsustainable industries and the case for community right to know and prevention' [online], Campaign for Alternative Industry Network, Greenpeace Southeast Asia, Global Community Monitor, October, http://www.bucketbrigade.net/downloads/thailand_toxic_cocktail.pdf (Accessed 25 March 2008).

Grenier, L. (1998) 'Working with indigenous knowledge. A guide for researchers', Ottawa, International Development Research Center.

Habermas, J. (1981) 'New social movements', *Telos*, no. 49, pp. 33–7.

Hirsch, P. (1997) *Seeing Forests for Trees: Environment and Environmentalism in Thailand*, Chiang Mai, Silkworm Books.

Hirsch, P. (1998) 'Community forestry revisited: messages from the periphery' in Victor, M., Lang, C. and Bornemeier, J. (eds) *Community Forestry at a Crossroads: Reflections and Future Directions in the Development of Community Forestry*, Bangkok, RECOFTC.

Jamison, A. (2001) *The Making of Green Knowledge: Environmental Politics and Cultural Transformation*, Cambridge, Cambridge University Press.

Jepson, P. (2005) 'Governance and accountability of NGOs', *Environmental Science and Policy*, vol. 8, pp. 515–24.

Johnson, T. (2006) 'E-waste dump of the world', *Seattle Times*, 6 April, http://seattletimes.nwsource.com/html/nationworld/2002920133_ewaste09.html (Accessed 5 October 2008).

Keck, M. E. and Sikkink, K. (1998) *Activists Beyond Borders: Advocacy Networks in International Politics*, Ithaca, NY, Cornell University Press.

Lang, M. T. (2003) 'Tai Ban research: local knowledge as negotiation in the policy process', *Thailand Human Rights Journal*, vol. 1, pp. 227–36.

Laungaramsri, P. (2002) 'Competing discourses and practices of "civil society": a reflection on the environmental movement in Thailand and some implications for the Mekong Region', presented at the Mekong Dialogue Workshop International transfer of river basin development experience: Australia and the Mekong Region, 2 September, Chiang Mai, Regional Centre for Sustainable Development and Social Science, Faculty of Social Sciences, Chiang Mai University.

Maneepong, C. (2006) 'Regional policy thinking and industrial development in Thai border towns', *Labour and Management in Development Journal*, vol. 6, no. 4.

McAdam, D. (1982) *Political Process and the Development of the Black Insurgency 1930–1970*, Chicago, IL, University of Chicago Press.

McAdam, D., McCarthy, J. D. and Zald, M. N. (1996) *Comparative Perspectives on Social Movements: Political Opportunities, Mobilizing Structures, and Cultural Framings*, Cambridge, Cambridge University Press.

McLaughlin, K. E. (2006) 'Chinese villages, poisoned by toxins, battle for justice', *Christian Science Monitor*, 23 June.

Melucci, A. (1989) *Nomads of the Present: Social Movements and Individual Needs in Contemporary Society*, Philadelphia, PA, Temple University Press.

Miller, B. (2000) *Geography and Social Movement: Comparing Antinuclear Activism in the Boston Area*, Minneapolis, MN, University of Minnesota Press.

Missingham, B. (2003a) 'Forging solidarity and identity in the Assembly of the Poor: from local struggles to a national social movement in Thailand', *Asian Studies Review*, vol. 27, no. 3, pp. 317–40.

Missingham, B. (2003b) *The Assembly of the Poor in Thailand: From Local Struggles to National Protest Movement*, Chiang Mai, Silkworm Books.

Pangsapa, P. and Smith, M. J. (2008) 'Political economy of Southeast Asian borderlands: migration, environment, and developing-country firms', *Journal of Contemporary Asia*, vol. 38, no. 4, pp. 485–514.

Pangsapa, P. and Smith, M. J. (2009) *Responsible Politics: Bringing Together Labor Standards, Environment, and Human Rights in the Global Corporate Economy*, New York, Palgrave Macmillan.

Pfirrman, C. and Kron, D. (1992) *Environment and NGOs in Thailand*, Bangkok, Thai NGO Support Project and Friedrich Naumann Stiftung.

Rootes, C. (2003) *Environmental Protest in Western Europe*, Oxford, Oxford University Press.

Sarre, P. and Jehlička, P. (2007) 'Environmental movements in space–time: the Czech and Slovak republics from Stalinism to post-socialism', *Transactions of the Institute of British Geographers*, vol. 32, no. 3, pp. 346–62.

Schlosberg, D. (1999) *Environmental Justice and the New Pluralism: The Challenge of Difference for Environmentalism*, Oxford, Oxford University Press.

Schlosberg, D. (2007) *Defining Environmental Justice: Theories, Movements and Nature*, Oxford, Oxford University Press.

Seager, J. (1993) *Earth Follies: Feminism, Politics and the Environment*, Washington, DC, Island Press.

Sivaraksa, S. (2002) 'Assembly of the Poor: Siam's poor take action on their own behalf', *Social Policy*, vol. 33, no. 1, pp. 47–9.

Smith, M. J. and Pangsapa, P. (2008) *Environment and Citizenship: Integrating Justice, Responsibility and Civic Engagement*, London, Zed Books.

Stein, R. (2004) *New Perspectives on Environmental Justice: Gender, Sexuality, and Activism*, Rutgers, NJ, Rutgers University Press.

Stimpson, P. (2000) 'Environmental attitudes and education in southern China' in Yencken, D., Fien, J. and Sykes, H. (eds) *Environment, Education and Society in the Asia-Pacific: Local Traditions and Global Discourses*, London, Routledge.

Suchman, M. C. (1995) 'Managing legitimacy: strategic and institutional approaches', *Academy of Management Review*, vol. 20, no. 3, pp. 571–610.

Tarrow, S. (1998) *Power in Movement: Social Movements and Contentious Politics*, Cambridge, Cambridge University Press.

Taylor, D. (2000) 'The rise of the environmental justice paradigm: injustice framing and the social construction of environmental discourses', *American Behavioural Scientist*, vol. 43, no. 4, pp. 508–80.

Tilly, C. (1994) 'Social movements as historically specific clusters of political performances', *Berkeley Journal of Sociology*, vol. 38, pp. 1–30.

Tilly, C. (2002) *Stories, Identities and Political Change*, Lanham, MD, Rowman and Littlefield.

Turner, J. and Hildebrandt, T. (2002) 'Navigating peace: forging new water partnerships', *China Environment Series*, issue 7, pp. 89–103.

Wang, C. and Ongley, E. D. (2004) 'Transjurisdictional water pollution management: the Huai River example', *Water International*, vol. 29, no. 3, pp. 290–8.

Wang, C. and Xu, K. (2007) 'Greening the courts: China's legal advocates giving voice to pollution victims and the environment', presentation at the China Environment Forum, Woodrow Wilson International Center, 11 April.

Westergaard, J. and Resler, H. (1976) *Class in a Capitalist Society*, New York, Penguin.

Wissenburg, M. (1998) *Green Liberalism: The Free and the Green Society*, London, UCL Press.

Chapter 3
Look South: environmental responses from developing countries

Sandrine Simon

Contents

1 Introduction

To develop the book's enquiry into how environmental policy could and should be improved, this chapter looks at the global South, and in particular at the poorest groups in the South. Although the numerous and varied collection of countries collectively described as the South contains the majority of the world's people, because it is characterised by low incomes and low, though varying, levels of development, it is more often thought to be in need of policy advice than to be a source of ideas. However, I argue that, in spite of poverty and environmental problems, it is possible to learn from the South, provided one avoids common misinterpretations.

There is a common tendency in the developed countries of the North to regard the South, and particularly its poorest people, as 'too poor to be green', and even to blame the victims of poverty and environmental degradation for their plight (see Figure 3.1). Accordingly, the conventional policy prescription for the South is to pursue export-oriented economic growth, seeking investment, technology transfer and skilled management

Figure 3.1
A few examples of environmental problems encountered in the South – from deforestation and desertification to pollution and flooding (clockwise from bottom left)

from outside. This priority is often accepted by elites in southern countries, and a minority of countries have actually experienced rapid economic growth, albeit with the environmental consequences discussed in the previous chapter.

This chapter argues that the conventional view is wrong in its diagnosis of the cause of southern problems and in its prescriptions. Instead, I present a different view, developed in four stages:

- First, I argue that the livelihoods of many people in the South, and especially of the rural poor, are more directly dependent on the environment than those in the North. Left to themselves, those livelihoods are often ecologically sustainable, since they have evolved over time and in relation to environmental variability.
- Second, I argue, as have many earlier parts of the course, that those livelihoods tend not to be left alone. Poor people are often wholly or partly dispossessed of their resource base by economic development projects, in which national or international interests claim to be making more efficient use of resources, but which often neglect the social and environmental consequences of the changes made. In this view, problems are not locally caused, but brought about by the fact that localities are drawn into the international economy in ways that benefit economically and politically powerful groups. The political nature of conventional development thinking is indicated by frequent local resistance movements.
- Third, contrary to conventional views, examples of international environmental leadership at the state level can be found in the South, provided that an alternative perspective of the North–South interaction in the environmental policy field – from the inside out – is adopted.
- Fourth, just as indigenous groups recognise that their livelihood is dependent on the environment, so economic calculation should recognise that economies are dependent on the environment, for resources and pollution disposal, and include these as costs rather than treat them as externalities. Similarly, costs to disadvantaged groups should be recognised, so that economic calculation takes account of the full range of costs and benefits, even where these are measured on different scales – for example, when sacred land is lost to mining projects. The approach to economics that takes account of these factors is called 'ecological economics'.

This outline presents an overview of the chapter's purposes, but without exploring the concepts and interpretations on which it rests. The argument is related back to ideas and examples in earlier parts of the course in Section 2 below. Further ideas and detail will be added in the subsequent four sections. Section 3 looks at the way in which communities' livelihoods in some southern contexts can be protected through traditional and indigenous practices that draw on the intimate knowledge of the interdependences between and within ecological and human systems (*course theme 1*). Section 4 focuses on ecological distributional conflicts that constitute the basis of numerous environmental problems in the South and highlights the role of power structures in influencing responses of southern environmental actors to these problems. Using biodiversity policy and green accounting as case studies, Section 5 then considers the conditions under which southern countries can aspire to international environmental leadership. Section 6 takes a look at the ways in which economic performance is defined and human needs are met while respecting environmental constraints, thus directly addressing *course themes 4* and 5.

1.1 Learning outcomes

This chapter should enable you to:

- understand the role of the poor themselves and of the international political economy as causes of environmental problems in the South
- identify responses to those environmental problems by local people and by some southern governments
- assess what could and should be done to address environmental problems in the South.

2 Characteristics of the South

I need to start this section by explaining what I mean by 'the South'. There is a tendency when referring to the many countries that have not achieved the status of 'developed', or 'high income', to use various homogenising labels, whether it be the 'developing world', 'the South' or, as was the case during the Cold War period, 'the Third World', as you saw in Book 2, Chapter 9. While these countries show some similarities, in having relatively low average incomes, poor nutrition, health, education and literacy, and hence shorter life expectancies, it is important to be aware of the great heterogeneity within and between the populations in this group of states in regard to the economy, environment, politics and culture. In this chapter, I will use the term 'South' both to refer to low-income countries as defined by the World Bank and to poor people in middle-income countries, who are just as numerous. Most of the case studies explored in the chapter relate to communities of sub-national level.

Activity 3.1

With this perspective in mind, think back to Book 2 and remind yourself of examples and ideas developed in relation to poor people in the South.

In my view, some key ideas and examples are:

Chapter 1, which challenges the idea that fast growing populations of poor people can straightforwardly be regarded as a cause of environmental degradation, pointing out that social context must be taken into account, especially inequality. The 2.5 billion people living on less than $2 per day show the extent of poverty, and concepts like post-colonialism and feminism help to interpret examples like El Salvador and Haiti, where concentration of land ownership drives poor people on to steep slopes.

Chapter 2 notes that poor people are often dependent on the environment for their livelihoods, and that policy often damages their prospects through exclusion or eviction – a point also made in Chapter 5 in relation to nature reserves.

Chapter 4 discusses the social construction of scarcity, especially through inequality in power and access. Tellingly, it suggests that allocation of costs and benefits depends on *'how resources are managed, by whom, in whose interests and with what outcomes'*.

Chapter 6 discusses the Green Revolution, and notes that while high-value exports have contributed to economic growth, they have also increased social inequality and chemical pollution. In Costa Rica, control of the lowlands by large landowners forces locals on to steep slopes and contributes to soil erosion. The chapter also notes that international trade in agricultural products is distorted by subsidies to developed world farmers and barriers to imports from poor countries – a point also made in Chapter 9.

Taken together, these references to the South suggest that the livelihoods of poor people, and their impacts on the environment, are deeply enmeshed in political and economic processes. This is linked to the history of the South by Raymond Bryant and Sinead Bailey:

> [The environmental crisis of the Third World] need[s] to be set against a long period of development that is rooted in distant colonial times, but which even today powerfully conditions the way in which human-environmental interaction takes place in the Third World. ... The role of the colonies in Asia, Africa and Latin America in this economic order was to provide precious metals, spices, tea, coffee, timber, minerals, cotton, groundnuts, copra and other products for consumption or manufacturing in Europe and North America. ... Colonial rule also led

> to political and administrative changes that fundamentally altered the ways in which states went about managing the peoples and environments under their jurisdiction. ... A colonial legacy of integration in a global capitalist economy, natural resource dependency, environmental degradation and centralised political control have conditioned environmental use and conflict in postcolonial times. That legacy ... continues to distinguish the Third World from elsewhere.
>
> (Bryant and Bailey, 1997, pp. 7–8)

Following independence, governments in the South typically found themselves with weak national economies, made up of extensive subsistence agriculture and craft production, set against a limited export sector, based on either minerals or commercial farms. Whether for idealistic reasons or for self-enrichment, elites felt a strong compulsion to pursue economic growth. As described in Book 2, Chapter 2, industrialisation was regarded as the best route towards development, but proved hard to achieve in most countries. Until the 1970s, it was common for southern governments to attempt to industrialise behind trade barriers, but as Book 2, Chapter 9 describes, the adoption of neoliberal policies ruled out such an approach, and markets were opened in most countries. While a small number of newly industrialising countries did develop export industries, most low-income countries were thrown back on resource exports as the only feasible route to economic growth. Since they lacked investment capital and technical expertise, they were dependent on firms from the developed world and had a strong incentive to make resources, whether land, forests or minerals, available to developers. The interests of subsistence farmers, who often lacked formal title to the land they used, were often curtailed.

Although most newly independent countries had democratic constitutions, in practice one-party rule, or even dictatorship, became more common. With economies dependent on a small number of major exports, the interests of elites and exporters became dominant and there was little incentive to respond to popular wishes. The extreme form of this syndrome has come to be known as 'the resource curse', since, with the exception of Middle Eastern oil exporters, countries dependent on mineral exports have typically grown more slowly than those without minerals, and in many cases corruption and conflict have laid waste lives and environments. Nicholas Shaxon (2007) documents the 'dirty politics of African oil', showing, for example, how massive oil exports have failed to trigger development in Nigeria, while making a minority fabulously rich and pollution impacts widespread (Figure 3.2). Since 2000, rising demand for many minerals has shown signs of generating economic growth, even in Africa, but it remains to be seen how long this will continue and how far the benefits will be distributed. Against this background there is a recurrent issue: the livelihood of large sections

Figure 3.2
Oil and development in Nigeria – the 'dirty politics of African oil'

of southern populations who depend for their survival on their environment and knowledge of it but are denied the benefits arising from the commercial exploitation of their environment and resources.

For several decades, addressing environmental issues in the South has always been associated with, and usually subordinated to, the need for economic development. Book 2, Chapter 7 highlighted the tension between economic growth and environmental protection as an important feature of the United Nations (UN) Conference on the Human Environment, held in Stockholm, Sweden, in 1972. Positions taken there led to the observation that 'the South is too poor to be green'.

This is a controversial statement as it depends on the definition of being 'green' and whether it is a result of necessity or free will. Arguably the poor are greener than the affluent as they consume fewer resources. See the cover of this book for a cartogram depicting ecological footprints of individual countries. Voluntarily reduced consumption will be discussed in Chapter 4

As described in Book 2, Chapter 9, the tensions between development and environment were the major concern of the 1987 Brundtland Report, which emphasised the need to overcome poverty and inequality in the South as a prerequisite for achieving sustainable development (SD) worldwide. It proposed a variety of interventions by governments and international agencies to pursue those objectives. However, by the time of the 1992 Rio conference these interventionist approaches had been abandoned in favour of a more market-based approach to environmental policy, an approach Steven Bernstein (2001) labels 'liberal environmentalism' and which is referred to, primarily in the European context, as 'ecological modernisation'.

Liberal environmentalism was introduced in Book 2, Chapter 9 and ecological modernisation in Book 1, Chapter 6

As you have gathered from the discussion of ecological modernisation in the course so far, despite some benefits, this interpretation of SD has its limits in formulating successful environmental responses. This situation was not helped by the fact that many southern actors, at least initially, only interpreted the concept of SD as a formal recognition of the need for economic development. If needed, the pursuit of economic growth was reconciled with environmental concerns using the argument that it would ultimately promote environmental protection – more affluent people tend to value the environment more highly, as the idea of the Environmental Kuznets Curve, introduced in Book 2, Chapter 2, proposes.

The 2002 Johannesburg WSSD was discussed in Book 2, Chapter 9.

After the UN World Summit on Sustainable Development (WSSD), held in Johannesburg in 2002, Paul Wapner (2003) concluded that the conference showed that a long-held belief had been abandoned – the belief that the North cared mainly about the environment and the South solely about development:

> After years of seeing the environment primarily as a luxury that the poor could ill afford, many southern governments have now picked up on the lead of their citizens in seeing the environment as the essential resource base on which economic life depends. ... At the WSSD, powerful voices from the North came out clearly in support of economic globalization. These governments made sure that the Johannesburg Declaration and Plan of Implementation did not contradict or otherwise undermine world trade agreements, and even suggested that the world look to such agreements as mechanisms for achieving the goals of the Summit.
>
> (Wapner, 2003, pp. 5–6)

Wapner's observations suggest that, rather than looking to northern interests to lead on environmental thought and practice, southern citizens might be offering a lead which environmental policy would do well to consider. The nature of this lead is presented in the following four sections.

3 Indigenous environmental practices

Environmentalist writing about the South, and especially about tribal and peasant peoples, has often taken extreme views: on the one hand such groups, and especially hunter-gatherers, have been romanticised as always and everywhere environmentally friendly; on the other hand, it has been common since Garret Hardin's 1968 essay to refer to 'the tragedy of the commons' as an inevitable result of the absence of individual property rights. This section will take a more nuanced view, investigating the claim that indigenous societies that have survived will have evolved sustainable practices which provide a livelihood adjusted to environmental resources and limits. If this is true, environmentalists can learn from them, even though they rarely see themselves as environmentalists, or are seen as such. The next subsection will

The tragedy of the commons was introduced in Book 1, Chapter 1, Box 1.2

present the views of some authors who have pressed this argument. The subsequent subsection moves on to present assessments from a particular approach to ecology.

3.1 The sustainability of indigenous livelihoods

A number of authors argue that indigenous southern approaches to environmental management are based on an intimate knowledge of ecological processes and of the functioning of ecosystems. These approaches are characterised by:

> embeddedness of knowledge in the local culture milieu; boundedness of local knowledge in space and time; the importance of community; lack of separation between nature and culture, and between subject and object; commitment or attachment to the local environment as a unique and irreplaceable place; and a non-instrumental approach to nature.
>
> (Berkes, 1999, p. 10)

By definition, indigenous groups have lived in an area for a generation or more. Hence they will have developed their lifestyles in relation to environmental resources and fluctuations over time, and also modified their initial environment in the process. This 'social construction of nature' was introduced in Book 2, Chapter 4. Since indigenous groups rely on their environment for their livelihood, they are likely to harvest a wide range of different products, for food of different kinds, clothes, tools, shelter and the requirements of cultural and religious ceremonies, and hence manage to encourage biodiversity. Their practices reflect, and contribute to, a detailed knowledge of their environment, and, because it reflects observation and experiment, **indigenous knowledge** is likely to contribute to sustainability (Figure 3.3) (Forest Peoples' Programme, 2008). Indigenous knowledge is knowledge generated by people in a certain area. It can include knowledge originating from elsewhere that has been internalised by local people through learning, testing and adaptation. It forms the basis of the art of identifying, unfolding and protecting local resources. It is specific to the local context. In addition, some practices seen by outsiders as irrational, such as taboos on eating certain animals or crops, or maintaining sacred groves, may help to conserve biodiversity, as well as promoting communication and cooperation within groups (Eder, 1996). In so doing, it is argued, people have learnt from ecosystems' resilience – that is their ability to absorb change and still persist – a claim evaluated in subsection 3.2.

Indigenous knowledge is knowledge generated by people in a certain area. It forms the basis of the art of identifying, unfolding and protecting local resources.

Figure 3.3
Traditional indigenous livelihoods in Amazonian forests

Fikret Berkes (1999) and Vandana Shiva (1994) argue that ecological sustainability of the forest is maintained through protecting its renewability and the diversity of species within it. The forest is not considered as only a source of wood but as a diverse habitat, influenced by the way in which water resources and land are being managed, as well as by the way in which human communities live in it, as shown in Box 3.1 and Activity 3.2. The forest managers are an integral part of their forest. Hence, they claim, the resilience of both society and ecosystem are enhanced. As Carl Folke et al. (2002, p. 4) explain, '[r]esilience moves beyond trying to control systems assumed to be stable to managing the capacity of human beings in relationship with natural systems to absorb shock and surprise, and to respond with creativity, novelty and innovation'. Management for resilience does not limit indigenous societies to reproducing traditional ideas and practices: they are able to innovate. One such innovation, tapping rubber from wild rubber trees in the Amazon, allowed local communities to make a living without forest clearance. Another example is provided in Activity 3.3.

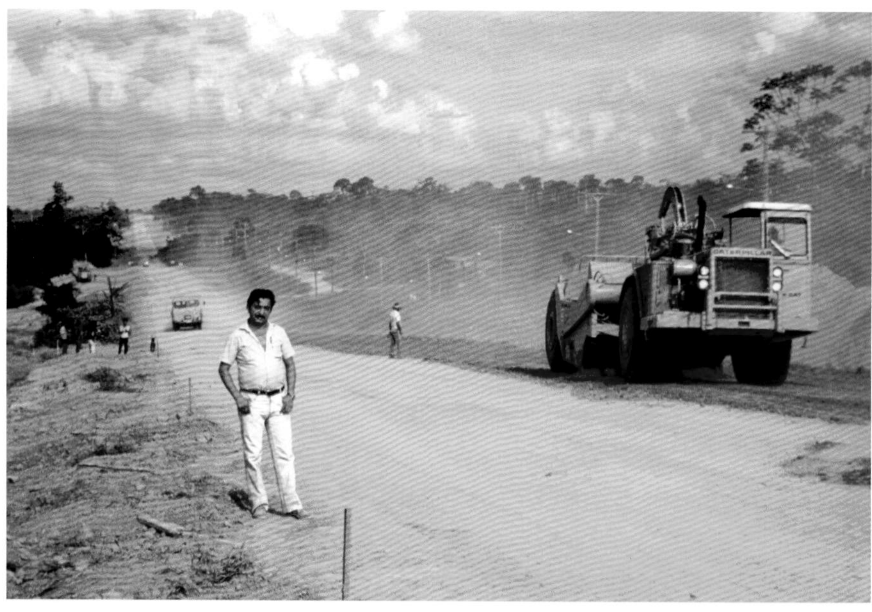

Figure 3.4
One of the most famous and popular environmental activists in Latin America, rubber tapper Chico Mendes, who was murdered in 1988

Activity 3.2

Read through Box 3.1 and note ways in which traditional forestry respects the principles of sustainability.

Box 3.1 Interdependences between and within society and nature in traditional forestry management

Examples of traditional forestry management can be found in various parts of the developing world, including India, Brazil and Central Africa (Figure 3.4). They have been studied by several authors, for example Berkes (1999) and Shiva (1994), who argue that they demonstrate living examples of ecologically, economically and socially sustainable practices. Their common characteristics can be described as follows:

- The forests they focus on have traditionally been central to civilisations and have been worshipped as such. Traditionally, there is no distinction between the spiritual, social, economic and political dimensions of the forest as a place to live in, protect and use to meet human needs. The traditional approach to forestry management is therefore, by definition, interdisciplinary.
- The diversity, harmony and self-sustaining nature of the forest formed the organisational principles guiding civilisation. In other words, the ways in which people use the forest resources respect renewal rates of the fauna and flora. Use of fire to regenerate the forest is directly guided by the observations of the natural cycles that are internal to the forest. People learnt that using forestry as 'integrated intervention' will ultimately help both the forest and the communities living from it.
- Traditional forestry includes various types of management of other 'components of the environment' such as land and water management. Although new academic research on these forms of integration often puts a question mark on how to integrate these various forms of management, traditional practices have always done so and this integration simply follows laws of nature.

Sources: Berkes (1999) and Shiva (1994)

Activity 3.3

Read the following extracts and note how the action undertaken by the fog catchers of Chungungo mimicked nature.

The fog catchers of Chungungo in Chile

In the extreme dryness of Chungungo, Chile, an ingenious use of a mysterious resource has helped the village get a handle on its chronic water problems. Chungungo is a small fishing village located about 279 miles (450 km) north of Santiago, huddled in the shadow of the coastal mountains. For decades, the 350 residents have lived with a chronic water shortage by transporting water over 30 miles (50 km) in an old tanker truck once or twice a week. The cost of the water was high and the quality suspect. In the mid-1980s, villagers working with Canadian developers devised a plan to mimic the action of the leaves of the town's eucalyptus trees. They reasoned that if the leaves could catch moisture, which in turn formed droplets, might not villagers construct nets which could likewise catch moisture? Today, using huge plastic mesh nets, Chungungo fog collectors actually catch the fog and harvest the droplets. Dripping down the mesh, the water droplets fall into the gutters. A pipeline then caries the water from the gutters down the mountain to tanks, and into the taps of homes and businesses in the village. And what's more, the water is clean. The old system of delivering water by trucks often brought disease, as the truck often carried other liquids in their tanks on other trips. [This new system of water collection] has improved the health of the entire community. In addition to domestic consumption, Chungungo's fog collectors now provide enough water for about 10 acres (4 hectares) of community vegetable gardens.

(Swanson, 2001, pp. 42–3)

...

The construction of the nets was originally funded by the Canadian International Development Research Centre. The success in Chungungo has spurred interest in the technology elsewhere. Fogcatchers have been installed in Islay province and in the Manchay hills on the coast of Peru, in collaboration with the Ministry of Agriculture's Instituto Nacional de Investigacion Agraria y Agro-Industrial and Asociacion TECNIDES respectively. In Ecuador, systems are operating at Pululahua and Pachamama Grande. Sites in Namibia and South Africa are also being tested for their suitability.

(IDRC, 1998)

Figure 3.5
The fog catching nets of Chunchungo, Chile

The technological solution relied on mimicking the natural action of eucalyptus leaves through the construction of the nets (Figure 3.5), rather than relying on the burning of fossil fuel and the use of transport to displace water from one place to another.

3.2 Resilience, biodiversity and sustainability: scientific debates

Recognition of the resilience of indigenous lifestyles has been developing in parallel with changing interpretations of ecology and its implications for development and sustainability. In the West, this debate dates back to a seminal paper published by an American ecologist (Holling, 1973), though in the 1970s similar concepts were also put forward in the Soviet Union (Saiko, 2001).

At that time, ecology aspired to the status of physics, and hence adopted methods seeking prediction and control, objectives which could most easily be realised by abstracting only a few variables. A particular idea was that ecosystems would develop towards an equilibrium state, and react to any changes, natural or social, by returning to that equilibrium. The initial concept of resilience was concerned with the time taken for the equilibrium state to restore itself after change. This is now described as 'engineering resilience' (Gunderson, 2000).

As the discipline of ecology developed, it became clear that many ecosystems can shift between a number of different stable states, in response to natural or social shocks, and that there is no single

Ecological resilience is the magnitude of disturbance a system can absorb before changing to another state.

equilibrium state. **Ecological resilience** is now defined as the magnitude of disturbance a system can absorb before changing to another state. It has long been argued that resilience is influenced by the biodiversity of an ecosystem, and recent research has clarified that this works in two ways. First, diversity of functional groups, for example, organisms with a particular feeding strategy, like nitrogen fixing plants or insect predators, is most important. Second, if each functional group includes a number of different species, total resilience is increased. However, while this diversity of functional groups and species contributes to the stability of the total ecosystem, it also allows large fluctuations in populations of particular species, since species can substitute for each other.

Garry Peterson et al. (1998) argued that it was insufficient to consider the stability or resilience of an individual ecosystem, since species may operate at different scales, and each ecosystem is therefore influenced by its neighbours and by larger or more distant ecosystems – for example, those which support migratory animals or birds at other seasons. Mosaics of diverse ecosystems are more resilient than more homogeneous landscapes. In the 1970s and 1980s Soviet geographers pursued similar objectives as they sought to define the integral resilience potential of various landscapes found within the former Soviet Union. Perel'man (1975, cited in Saiko, 2001, p. 12) defined **landscape** as 'a complex dynamic system of the Earth's surface, in which living organisms and inorganic matter penetrate into each other, are very closely linked and deeply interdependent'. Biological components of landscape, particularly vegetation cover, were found to be the main stabilising force of nature (Saiko, 2001, pp. 22–3). Accordingly, the least resilient landscapes, least likely to withstand disturbance, were those in the Arctic and the hot dry lands of Central Asia, while the most resilient were those in landscapes with deciduous forests.

Landscape, in the Soviet science conceptualisation, was a complex dynamic system of the Earth's surface, in which living organisms and inorganic matter penetrated into each other, were very closely linked and deeply interdependent.

Joern Fischer et al. (2006) have applied existing knowledge about diversity, resilience and stability to propose 'ten guiding principles for commodity production landscapes'. They note that overall resilience is often reduced where commercial crops are substituted for natural vegetation, and that resulting areas are more vulnerable to disturbances like drought or insect infestation. Half of their ten principles deal with landscape patterns: leave large patches of native vegetation; link them with corridors; create buffers around sensitive areas; use similar structures for planted ecosystems as in the native ones; maintain landscape heterogeneity.

The other five deal with processes: continue disturbance regimes, such as periodic burning of native vegetation; maintain key species; control over-abundant or invasive species; maintain species at risk of

Figure 3.6
Monoculture production of palm oil

extinction; minimise threats like pollution or hunting. These principles are far from the normal pattern of commercial landscapes, which tend towards monocultures – large areas dominated by a single crop (Figure 3.6). They are much more consistent with the landscapes occupied by indigenous groups, where interventions are smaller scale and more heterogeneous.

Activity 3.4

Re-read Section 5 of Book 2, Chapter 5. How does its account of the design and management of protected areas relate to the ten principles identified above? How does the local community best contribute to biodiversity conservation?

The two accounts are highly complementary. Protected areas are no longer thought of as isolated islands, but as core areas protected by buffer areas and linked by corridors. Both approaches include conservation of biodiversity and keystone species. In contrast to approaches that exclude local people from protected areas, Chapter 5 advocates the potential benefits of co-management, and especially of community conserved areas (CCAs), since they tend to conserve both bio- and cultural diversity. How might the concept of resilience take this further?

The literature on resilience has become interdisciplinary, as scholars from fields related to ecology began to question whether the same concepts could be used on social groups as well as on ecosystems.

Figure 3.7
Sea-coast in central Vietnam

Neil Adger (2000) summarised the literature on social resilience and reported a study in coastal Vietnam (Figure 3.7). He noted a number of sources that suggest a connection between ecological resilience and social resilience where the group concerned is dependent on local ecological resources. However, social resilience is also influenced by institutional structure and practice, which is not solely dependent on ecology, but also affected by perceived legitimacy and inclusivity. Noting that many coastal ecosystems were being degraded by inappropriate privatisation, he investigated coastal communities in Vietnam and concluded that dependence on a resilient ecosystem was helpful in resisting natural shocks, but not in the face of state development policy. Left alone, or with state support, indigenous groups can be innovative in the face of shocks, but all too often their political weakness leaves them exposed to problems created by more powerful interests, as discussed in Section 4.

3.3 Implications for the North

Interdisciplinary work on social and ecosystem resilience allows us to go beyond stereotypes of indigenous societies to identify land management practices that contribute to diversity, resilience and sustainability. While many indigenous societies follow these kinds of practice, others do not, either because of their internal processes, or because they have come under pressure from outsiders interested in their resources.

There are two implications for the North. First, any interventions in the South should aim to value, foster and extend the good practice that already exists, rather than assume that radical change is needed. Second, these land management standards also apply to developed societies, few of which reach the standards of resilience recommended by ecologists. Hence, developed societies themselves have much to learn from the debate about ecological resilience.

As Gerald Marten (2001, p. 9) argues, **ecologically sustainable development** is about keeping ecosystems healthy and interacting with ecosystems in ways that allow them to maintain sufficient functional integrity to continue providing humans and all other creatures in the ecosystem the food, water, shelter and other resources that they need. Damaged ecosystems that lose their capacity to meet basic human needs close off opportunities for economic development and social justice. A healthy society gives equal attention to ecological sustainability, economic development and social justice because they are mutually reinforcing.

Ecologically sustainable development is about keeping ecosystems healthy and interacting with ecosystems in ways that allow them to maintain sufficient functional integrity to continue providing humans and all other creatures in the ecosystem the food, water, shelter and other resources that they need.

4 Resistance to development projects and defence of local communities' livelihoods

Although indigenous environmental practices contain valuable knowledge on how to manage and live within local peoples' environments, they could become rapidly marginalised and ultimately lost if their value is not recognised and if they are not adopted by more powerful actors capable of influencing environmental policy processes. Understanding the ecological principles of resilience to natural or economic shocks and designing environmental practices that can deal with these shocks cannot be done effectively without understanding the power dynamics among environmental actors – in other words, understanding how resources are managed, by whom and in whose interest. These are concerns of political ecology – an analytical perspective employed by geographers, social anthropologists and political scientists in researching local resource management conflicts in the South.

4.1 Political ecology

In Book 2, Chapter 3 by Jessica Budds you learnt how poor citizens of New Orleans were disproportionately affected by Hurricane Katrina. Drawing on insights from political economy, political ecology emerged in the 1970s and 1980s out of similar concerns about the 'Third World' poor suffering disproportionately from natural hazards (critical-hazards analysis). Third World political ecology (TWPE) was critical of neo-Malthusianism, the influential discourse in the 1970s and 1980s. As Claudia Aradau showed in Book 2, Chapter 1, neo-Malthusianism attributed the plight of the Third World poor during extreme geophysical events to 'overpopulation' or 'population explosion'. In contrast, Third World political ecologists argued that 'the preoccupation with population ... diverted attention away from the real problem: uneven economic development and the drain of resources from South to North, which together made communities in the developing world highly vulnerable to phenomena like droughts and floods' (Bryant, 2001, p. 151).

After the initial focus on critical-hazards analysis, TWPE embarked on systematic research into local but long-term environmental and social problems affecting poor farmers in the South. Instead of relying on demographics as an explanatory factor, Third World political ecologists highlighted the importance of political and economic factors: 'political ecology focused on the way meso and macro scale political and economic forces set the context for local environmental action and interaction, most commonly amongst primary producers' (Robbins, 2003, p. 643). The central question political ecologists sought to answer was whether it was 'possible to create conservation policy that accounts for environmental dynamism and that does not deny the rights of vulnerable people' (Zimmerer, 2000, cited in Robbins, 2003, p. 644). TWPE analyses drew on concepts of unequal power relations and large-scale societal structures and related the misfortunes of developing countries' peasantry to the Third World's structural subordination to the 'First World'. As Noel Castree (2005, p. 83) stated, 'political ecologists wished to alter those relations and structures so that southern poor farmers would not be forced into degrading the resources and environments upon which they depended for their livelihoods'. Thus, in terms of the distinction between the two analytical approaches to social change needed to solve environmental problems which were introduced in Chapter 1 of this book – problem solving and critical approaches – TWPE clearly falls in the latter category.

In this section I will focus on examples of environmental responses as defence of rights and livelihoods. As Juan Martinez-Alier argued:

> only in the south have large masses of people engaged in environmental conflicts, while fending for themselves. As explained by Ramachandra Guha (2000, p. 106), commercial tree plantations,

> oil drilling, gold and copper mining, and large dams all damage the environment, and they also, and to their victims more painfully, constitute a threat to livelihoods. The opposition to these interventions is as much a defence of livelihood as an 'environmental' movement in the narrow sense of the term.
>
> (Martinez-Alier, 2002, p. 205)

Indigenous groups' sustainable lifestyle and resource management are often considered by both southern governments and international development agencies and financial institutions as backward and in need of modernisation. As you learnt in Book 2, Chapter 2, many southern governments have vigorously pursued industrialisation as a way to economic growth. Part of this strategy has been the promotion of large-scale infrastructure projects such as dams. Due to their lack of legal, economic and political power, indigenous groups have often been displaced and pushed to marginal land or, as you saw in Book 2, Chapter 3, to informal settlements in large cities. As Bryant and Bailey explain, development projects often result in marginalisation of local communities:

> This process occurs when poor grassroots actors such as farmers or shifting cultivators are pushed onto lands that are economically marginal as a result of their marginal political and economic status. Desperate to extract a living from such lands, these actors intensify production but in the process often only increase the land's economic marginality (i.e. reduced capability). The vicious cycle continues since the prospect of an actor deriving a livelihood from the land is thereby diminished.
>
> (Bryant and Bailey, 1997, p. 32)

4.2 Resistance to the Sardar Sarovar dam

The case of the Thai Assembly of the Poor examined in the previous chapter also showed how indigenous groups whose sustainable resource management comes under threat by development projects can resist these projects in defence of their livelihood. In this section, I shall develop this theme further, focusing on opposition to a large-scale project in India (Figure 3.8).

Activity 3.5

Read the following case study of resistance to a dams project in India and identify different types of actors, their interests and power positions.

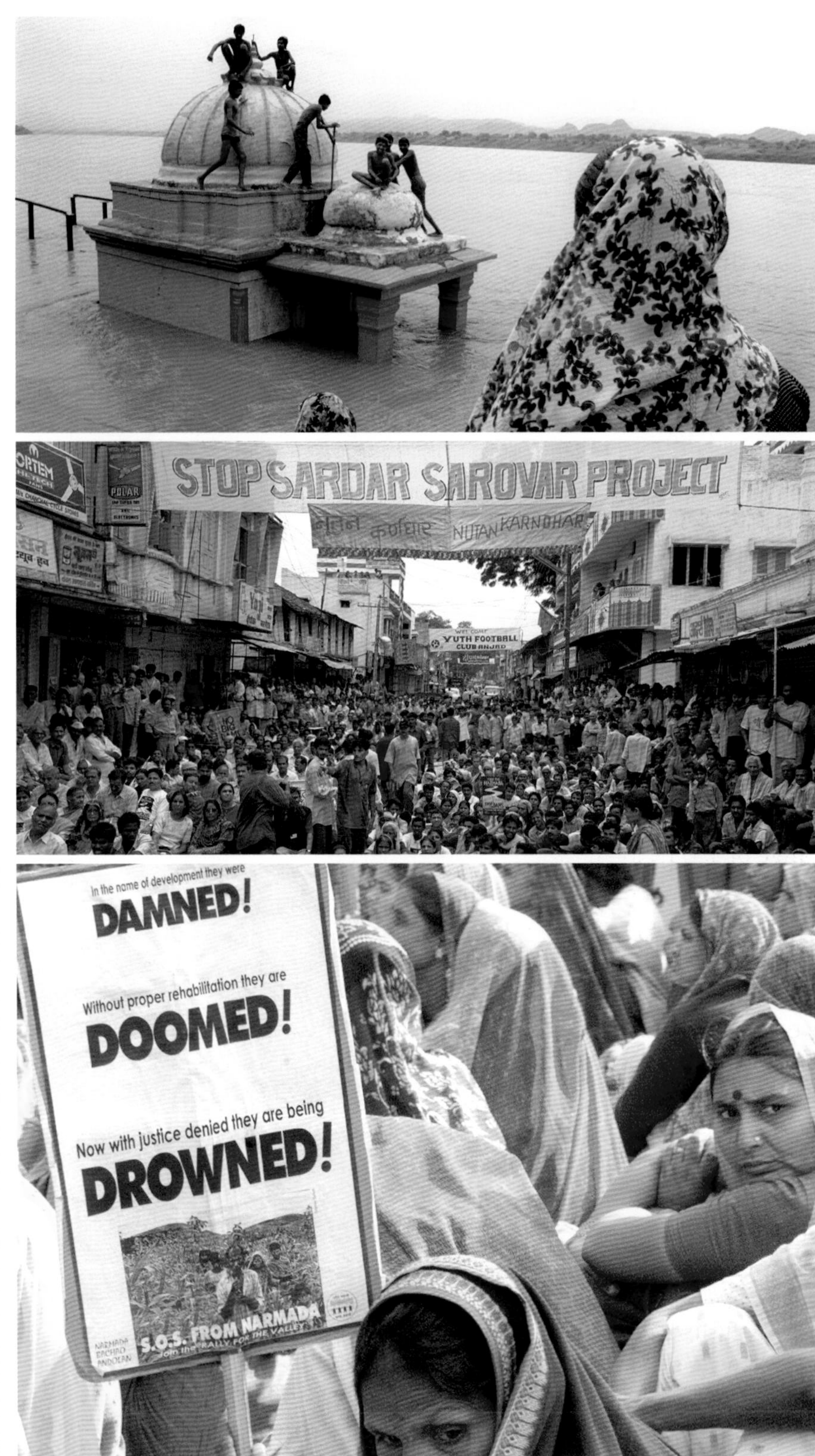

Figure 3.8
The devastating effects of large dam construction in India – environmental damages and social upheaval

As you learnt in Book 2, Chapter 2, Jawaharlal Nehru's development policy referred to large dams as the 'temples of modern India': politically, their construction became a symbol of modernisation. In the post-independence period, the environmental implications of these large projects were not an issue, but more recently, the opposition to large dams has grown considerably. With that in view, the World Commission on Dams (WCD) published a report in 2000 in which it noted that as development priorities changed and experience accumulated, various groups argued that the expected economic benefits of large dams were not being obtained and that major environmental economic and social costs were not being taken into account (Rangachari et al., 2000). The adverse social impacts, in particular, although shocking in their magnitude (the 4289 Indian dams have, over the years, displaced between 16 and 38 million people, according to various estimates), were either not reflected at all or only partly reflected in the economic analyses of previously built dams.

The case of one dam is of particular relevance here. As the India case study reported (Rangachari et al., 2000, p. 28), 'few large dams have aroused as much controversy or such a bitter campaign of hatred as the Sardar Sarovar Project. The project was one of those dams envisaged by Nehru in the 1940s. It has been likened by some to a disaster and yet regarded by others as the most desired and most delayed solution to their problems'. It is the largest of the thirty large dams to be built on the 1321 km long Narmada River as part of the Narmada Valley Development Project, which has been the object of disputes between a range of actors, including three Indian states (Madhya Pradesh, Maharashtra and Gujarat), since its inception in the 1960s.

The government claimed that it would make the irrigation of more than 1.8 million ha (mostly in Gujarat) possible. The opponents countered that the benefits generated by the construction of the dam were grossly exaggerated and scientifically incorrect. Instead, they argued, the construction of the dam would cause large-scale abuse of human rights and displacement of many poor and underprivileged communities. In India, the environmental impact assessment (EIA), which had become a statutory requirement in 1994, was rapidly made optional again. No impact analysis was consequently conducted for the Sardar Sarovar.

At the beginning of the 1990s, a series of local non-violent protests took place, using a variety of tactics pioneered by Gandhi in struggles against British rule. They included mass demonstrations, strikes, blockades, and 'shaming the state'. The latter included hunger strikes, mass incarcerations and threats of 'water burials' – remaining in villages as the water level rose (Guha and Martinez-Alier, 1997). Most of these responses were aimed at the Indian government, but they were also calculated to put pressure on the World Bank (which was funding the project) to constitute an independent review committee. The research of the Bank's commission of enquiry concluded that both social and ecological costs were considerable and the Bank withdrew from the project.

The construction of the Sardar Sarovar was halted for a time but, in October 2000, the Supreme Court of India allowed an immediate re-start of the construction of the dam. Although the Narmada Water Dispute Tribunal Award stated that land should be made available to the communities that would be displaced at least a year in advance of submergence, this decision was violated in 2006 when the Supreme Court allowed the raising of the dam even though thousands of families were yet to be relocated and 35,000 more faced displacement. Despite the overwhelming evidence of social and ecological damage, the protests in Delhi and a twenty-day hunger strike, the Supreme Court and government of India turned a blind eye to the fundamental injustice caused by the construction of this dam.

At this point you should consider your response to Activity 3.5.

A number of actors, both Indian and international, appeared in the case study: non-governmental organisations (NGOs), local communities, the WCD, writers and journalists – such as Vandana Shiva and Arundhati Roy (Figure 3.9), the World Bank, the Indian government, the Supreme Court of India and the Narmada Water Dispute Tribunal. They were involved in

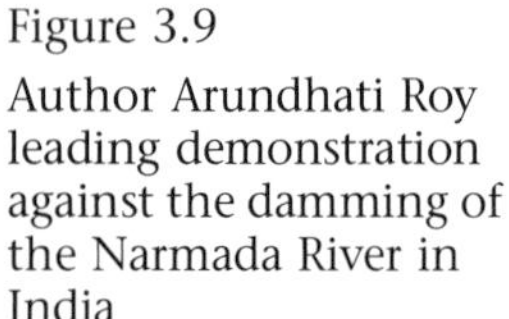

Figure 3.9
Author Arundhati Roy leading demonstration against the damming of the Narmada River in India

a range of conflicts – between actors and between ways of thinking and ways of envisaging development. These manifested themselves in the forms of disputes, strikes and non-violent demonstrations, court cases and controversies, which took place either in India or in other parts of the world, and through pieces of writing, for instance, aimed at raising awareness of the reasons for the opposition against the construction of large dams. As you saw, local communities' opposition to the project took the form of resistance against the threats to local people's livelihoods imposed by local and national governments. As Martinez-Alier (2002, p. 211) put it, there had often been a 'palpable sense of betrayal, a feeling that the government has let the poor down by taking the side of the rich, whether nationals or foreigners'.

You have seen in this section that the political ecology perspective offers an insight into conflicts over management of local resources that come under pressure from transnational economic forces and in which local communities respond to changes in state policies. Paul Robbins (2003, p. 643) argued that while in practice the state and its policies play a pivotal role in these conflicts, from a political ecology viewpoint the state is usually seen either as a somewhat passive conduit for market penetration and bringing contractualised production into local exchange relations, or as a modernist menace guiding large-scale ecological change. This raises the question whether the state in the South can act as an agent of policy innovation. This is the topic I will be exploring in the next section.

5 Southern environmental leadership?

The previous section showed that development projects in the South often fail to consider social and environmental impacts and can be dubiously effective. This section explores two examples of what by conventional accounts seems counterintuitive – southern international environmental leadership. First, you will take a look at the development of biodiversity policy in two Latin American countries. Second, you will consider the case of green accounting in southern Africa as an alternative policy-making tool and a top-down, research-based approach aimed at translating people's needs and ecological requirements for a more just approach to economics and economic performance. In the terms introduced in Chapter 1 of this book, both case studies represent the problem-solving approach.

5.1 Biodiversity conservation in Latin America

Most literature on environmental policy making in the South falls into two types of analysis. One, which you encountered in the previous section of this chapter – political ecology – draws on political economy.

It relates local resources management conflicts to larger, typically supranational processes of exploitation, and studies threats these processes pose to local communities' livelihood. In some cases, local resistance actors benefit from the strategy of scaling up their struggle by forming alliances with supranational, North-based NGOs and other actors. The other type of analysis of environmental policy making in the South, introduced in Book 1, Chapter 4 and in Book 2, Chapters 5 and 7, is international cooperation. It draws on international studies' interest in the sources of cooperation and conflict among sovereign states. The analyses conducted under the international cooperation perspective focus on the effect individual international environmental agreements have in developing countries. Both analytical perspectives tend to underestimate the importance of studying policy developments at the state level. They also perceive the southern state as a rather passive recipient of policy ideas and approaches emanating from international – largely North-controlled – economic and environmental systems of governance.

In his effort to explain how biodiversity policies in two Latin American countries – Costa Rica and Bolivia (Figure 3.10) – were transformed from non-existent to exemplars for other states in the South, Paul Steinberg (2001) reversed this perspective and instead of studying how these international agreements and institutions affected domestic policy outcomes he adopted the 'inside out' and long-term perspective to exploring international influences on domestic developments. His ambition was to go beyond the accounts that see policy change in developing countries merely as more or less successful compliance with activities driven by North-based actors, whether it be NGOs, governments or international organisations.

Drawing on insights from comparative politics and public policy theory, he set out to scrutinise two commonly held views: first, that southern states are 'too poor to care about global environmental problems', and second, that national governments are both unwilling and unable to play a constructive role in natural resource management (Steinberg, 2001, p. 195), an assumption underpinning much of the TWPE research.

Seeking to uncover why southern states sometimes play a constructive role, Steinberg started his research by identifying the most important instances of biodiversity policy reform in Bolivia and Costa Rica (see Table 3.1). He then proceeded to analyse the relative contributions that domestic and international players have made to these outcomes, identified who these players were and what resources and strategies they used to promote policy change (Steinberg, 2001, pp. 7 and 197).

Table 3.1 Biodiversity policy accomplishments in Bolivia and Costa Rica

Bolivia	Costa Rica
World's first debt-for-nature swap	National Biodiversity Institute (INBio)
World's largest forest-based carbon offset initiative	Among the world's best national park systems
Experimental local/indigenous park management	Strong environment ministry
Rapidly growing protected areas system	Environmental commission of the Ministry of Foreign Relations
National Environmental Fund	Environmental legislation/ constitutional amendment
Leader in international efforts to protect vicuña	Pioneer in the development of nature tourism
Innovative forestry legislation	Advisory Commission on Biodiversity (COABio)
Gradual strengthening of environmental ministry	Leader in joint implementation projects
National biodiversity conservation agency	Leader in debt-for-nature swaps
Leader in efforts to list mahogany under CITES	National Parks Foundation
Total ban on trade in domestic species	Administrative reform of park system

Source: Steinberg, 2001, p. 132

Activity 3.6

What insights do resource mobilisation and political process – the two theoretical approaches that you encountered in the previous chapter in connection with environmental movements – offer to the investigation of change in national biodiversity policy in the South?

Steinberg (2001, p. 7) argued that the opportunities and resources influencing environmental policy in southern countries are of two types: those closely associated with a given domestic political system, and those whose essential productive dynamic resides beyond that society's borders. The former are domestic political resources, including personal and political contacts and the knowledge of bureaucratic power

Figure 3.10
Biodiversity richness in Bolivia and Costa Rica

structures. The latter are external financial and ideational resources. The international sphere is a source of scientific and policy ideas and innovations (norms, evaluations, modes of governance) that interact with domestic norms and understandings. To achieve their goals, actors involved in policy change need to be able to take advantage of opportunities offered by national political structures to mobilise resources at home and abroad. The two spheres of influence framework involves 'elements of both structure and agency – of relatively immovable constraints on social action, and the significant degree of

The concepts of structure and agency were introduced in Book 1, Chapter 1 creativity and entrepreneurship that individuals exercise within these constraints' (Steinberg, 2001, p. 198).

The main finding of Steinberg's research was that while the bulk of funding of environmental groups and state conservation institutions in Bolivia and Costa Rica came from abroad, and domestic biodiversity policy actors relied on external expertise and know-how, those who drove biodiversity policy change – who started the environmental groups, who created the regulatory agencies, who convinced the politicians to take action, who led the protests – came from inside the two countries. Steinberg argued that the central role in this several decades long process was played by **bilateral activists** – Costa Rican and Bolivian professionals who operated simultaneously in both international and domestic spheres of influence and possessed both close ties to domestic politics and a broad exposure to international resources and ideas. Bilateral activists were both steeped in international scientific ecological and conservation discourses, frequently interacting with their counterparts abroad, and embedded in domestic political culture and networks. They were as likely to work for environmental NGOs as for governments or universities and often moved between the two. Thus, the political dynamics behind Bolivia's and Costa Rica's biodiversity leadership was 'bureaucratic manoeuvring by domestic policy reformers ..., who engage[d] in lesson-learning and experimentation, behind-the-scenes mobilization of personal contacts, and persistent policy entrepreneurship over a period of decades' (Steinberg, 2001, p. 205).

Bilateral activists are professionals who operate simultaneously in both international and domestic spheres of influence and possess both close ties to domestic politics and a broad exposure to international resources and ideas.

The process of biodiversity policy change in Costa Rica and Bolivia developed in several stages. In reality, these stages overlap; I am presenting them here as separate processes for analytical reasons. This transformation did not take place simultaneously in the two countries. While the process followed the same sequence in Bolivia, each of these stages took place about a decade later than in Costa Rica. The initial stage was the exchange of ideas between small groups of foreign and domestic experts and activists at a range of settings including conferences, universities and research cooperation. The second stage involved the process of translation in which the key concept was the 'fit' between an idea being considered for import from the foreign into the domestic setting and the cultural and political orientation of a particular southern society. Some ideas travelled more easily than others due to their better fit. In the third stage, the ideas of small groups of domestic experts and activists were adopted by state authorities and social movements. Legislative, policy and institutional changes at the state level were usually preceded by the development of new study programmes, training sessions for various groups of professionals and the establishment of civic environmental organisations (Steinberg, 2001, p. 202).

Activity 3.7

It seems fitting to conclude this section by inviting you to consider a question suggested at the beginning: To what extent does the analytical framework developed in this section in connection with Costa Rica's and Bolivia's biodiversity policies apply elsewhere in the South?

Biodiversity hotspots were introduced in Book 2, Chapter 5

The location of the majority of the world's biodiversity hotspots in the South and of the centres of funding and ecological and biological expertise in the North warrants interaction between the two. The international sphere of influence – the sources of external funding and scientific expertise based in the North – is likely to be relevant to the majority of developing countries. Translating imported ideas to make them compatible with the domestic political culture and transform them into policies and institutions when opportunities arise requires the systematic and skilful activity of domestic bilateral activists. While this analytical framework is applicable generally, the performance of individual developing countries in the development of biodiversity policy will vary. Among other country-specific factors, much will depend on the historical and social context. For example, Steinberg (2001, p. 199) pointed out that many former British colonies in Africa and Asia are in the immediate future unlikely to emulate successes of the two Latin American countries due to their more recent colonial experience and the association of early nature conservation initiatives with British rule. However, in the long run collaborative approaches to biodiversity policy development are likely to be more successful than the neo-colonial approaches taken by some international charities which you learnt about in Book 2, Chapter 5.

5.2 Linking economy and environment: green accounting

A second way in which some southern states have led is in the application of green accounting. The events and ideas discussed in Section 4 suggest that southern countries, even more than their northern counterparts, need better ways of linking economic policy to environmental and social realities. Ideally, these should diminish the difficulties of negotiating adoption of environmental policies. This subsection considers an approach that is international in scope but that is especially relevant to the South.

Every functioning state in the world makes some use of the system of national accounts (SNA) – the internationally accepted way of recording economic activity. At a minimum, data is supplied to international agencies, where it is used to make decisions about aid and other development assistance. In most countries it is also used to influence economic and development policy. Most governments use one feature of the SNA – gross domestic product (GDP), defined as the total market value of all goods and services produced within a country in the calendar year – as a major objective for policy, believing it measures total economic activity, and averaged over the population, indicates the level of prosperity and development.

Gross domestic product (GDP) was introduced in Chapter 1 of this book.

Unfortunately, the SNA, and hence GDP, is an incomplete measure, with deficiencies that are particularly serious for economies in which subsistence activities and resource exports play major roles, as is typically the case in the South. As explained by Joy Hecht (1999), the SNA does not measure:

- the value of non-traded activities, such as subsistence production
- the value of ecosystem services, from water purification to pollution absorption
- the depreciation of natural capital, such as deforestation or mineral exports.

As well as omitting these factors, GDP includes all costed economic activities, and hence rises where a pollution event, such as a tanker wreck, requires insurance payouts and expenditure on cleaning up, and counts the income from timber export without noting the reduction in the stocks of trees. In effect it treats any economic activity, however unwelcome or harmful, as a good thing, does not identify the costs of pollution controls, and omits many valued social and environmental services because they are not paid for.

Some efforts have been made to address these deficiencies, initially in high-income countries, with Norway as a leader, but from the 1990s spreading internationally and including pioneer applications in southern Africa. The nearest approach to an international standard is the UN's System for Integrated Environmental and Economic Accounting (SEEA) (UN, 2003). This extends the SNA by recording initial natural capital and changes over each time period, allowing a variety of 'greened' indicators to be calculated. However, some of the environmental data are included as physical quantities and the system allows different countries to use different measures and ways of valuing them. Use of market values to measure changes to capital stocks is criticised by environmentalists, who suggest that market values don't reflect the true value of nature, while economists argue that it allows the use of market instruments to internalise costs such as pollution (Bartelmus, 2008).

A major project to apply the SEEA in southern Africa began in 1995 and with initial comparisons and connections between Botswana, Lesotho,

Namibia and South Africa. Glenn-Marie Lange et al. (2003) pointed out that inclusion of resource stocks in the accounts of these three countries related directly to the concept of SD, since resource exports reduced economic wealth unless revenues were captured and invested in human or manufactured capital within the country. They contrasted Botswana, where revenues had been invested, with Namibia, where fish stocks had declined dramatically, but revenues could not be recovered from international fishing fleets, and noted that Botswana's economy had grown at 5 per cent per annum while Namibia's had stagnated.

South Africa has made advances in accounting for the whole range of goods and services provided by forests, rather than just the value of timber in commercial plantations. Non-timber products include honey, flowers, food, livestock grazing and traditional medicines, and non-marketed products are the highest value sector of forest production. The accounts also include a measure for the effects of forest on water supply, revealing that commercial plantations absorb much more rainfall than native species, reducing runoff to downstream areas.

A pioneering feature of the southern African accounts is that they treat water internationally, extending coverage to the whole of the Orange River Basin. All four countries suffer water scarcity, but until the 1990s supplied water to their biggest users, agriculture, at subsidised rates, especially in South Africa, where irrigated commercial farms, mostly in minority hands, were the main beneficiaries. All four countries are moving towards full-cost pricing to encourage more rational decisions about use of water. Botswana's GDP per cubic metre of water was five times higher than South Africa's.

Considerable efforts were put into designing the national water policy in South Africa in the post-apartheid Reconstruction and Development Programme (1994). With firm intentions to take not only economic efficiency but also equity into consideration when formulating water policies, Botswana, Lesotho, Namibia and South Africa aimed at changing the provision of water services to the poor, the way water is priced and allocated, and the way water rights are defined. They all adopted integrated water management in order to do so, thus recognising that economic considerations must be incorporated into water management decisions, but also that water should be allocated to the most economically productive activities only once basic human needs and ecosystems' requirements have been met.

Achieving this requires regular assessment of the economic costs and benefits of water use by each economic sector, as well as alternative means of supply. The construction of water accounting helped these four countries to achieve this goal. In particular, as Lange et al. (2007) explained, these accounts link water statistics (use, supply, resources, discharges of pollutants) directly to national income accounts. They provide aggregate indicators that show warning signs of any trend that may be unsustainable or socially undesirable. They also provide detailed sectoral indicators that shed light on sources of pressure on water resources, opportunities for reducing the pressure, and contribution of economic incentives to the problem and possible solutions. Because water accounts are linked to national income accounts, they can also be used for more complex economic analysis and modelling to project future water demands and evaluate different policy options for meeting those demands, such as pricing reforms, water efficiency improvements, waste water reuse and recycling, and demand management.

The appropriate management of transboundary rivers can only be addressed at the regional level, taking into account the way water is used by all riparian states. In contrast to national accounts, constructing water accounts for a river basin poses special challenges because the basin does not always correspond neatly to administrative areas for which economic and other relevant data are compiled (see Box 3.2).

Box 3.2 The water accounts of the Orange River Basin

In each country, water is not treated as a single resource or commodity as many types of water are represented, including surface, groundwater, perennial rivers and ephemeral or seasonal rivers stored in dams. The national water accounts provide spatially disaggregated data that can be readily mapped onto the Orange River Basin (see the map of the Orange River Basin in Figure 3.11). In order to compare the role of each riparian state, the Orange River Basin water accounts are separated into four geographical areas (South Africa, Botswana, Namibia and Lesotho).

The water accounts for the Orange River Basin include a supply and use table in physical units (km^3) disaggregated by the natural source of water. In addition to the use by economic activities, ecological requirements are included where available. South Africa's water policy specifies that water needed for ecosystem health is a priority use, hence the inclusion of an ecological reserve in the calculation of surface water yield (defined as SWY= mean annual runoff + storage ecological reserve – river losses [evaporation and seepage, alien vegetation use] + urban runoff). This is not the case in Botswana or Namibia.

Source: FAO, 1997

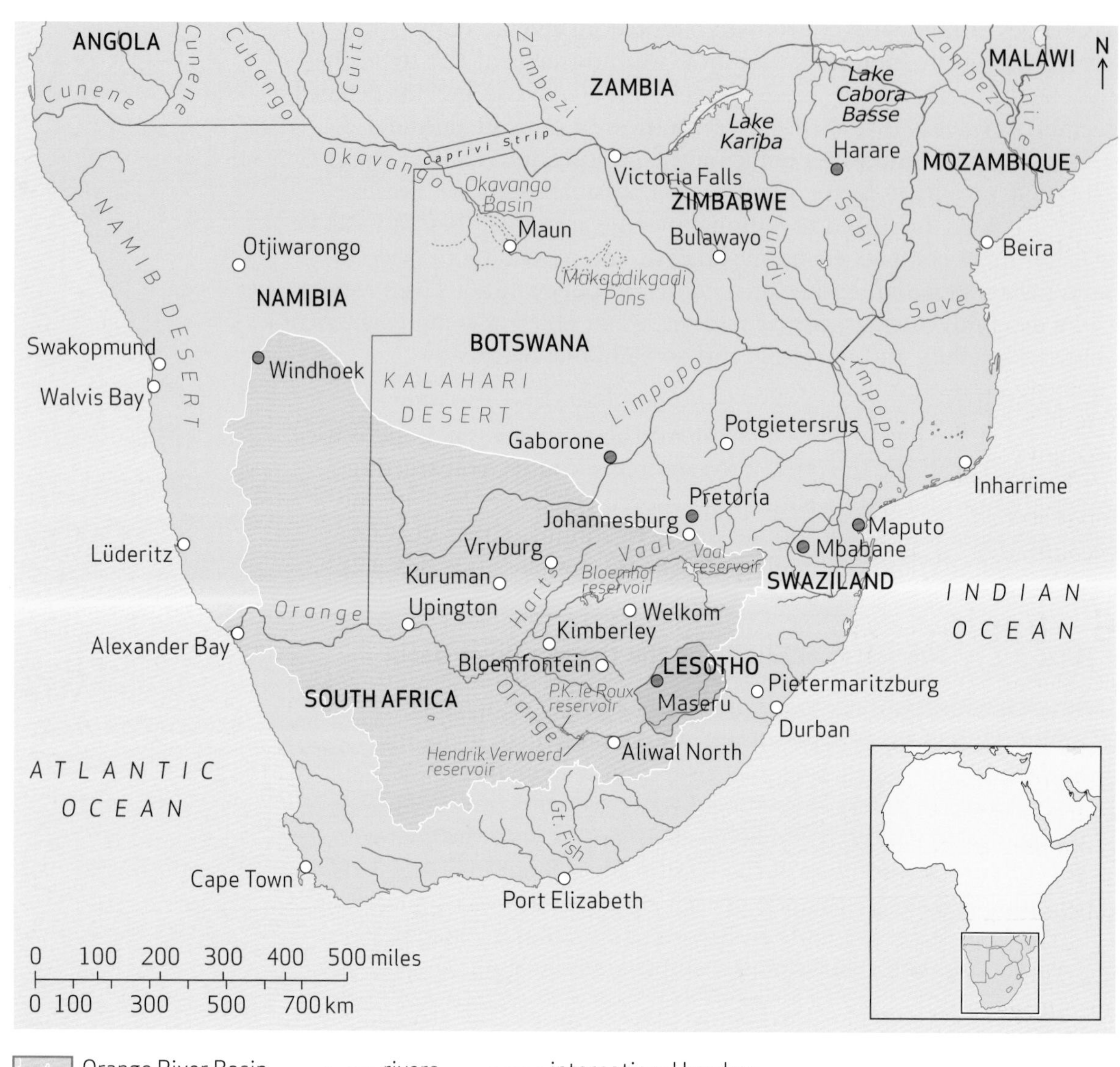

Figure 3.11
The Orange River Basin (Source: FAO, 1997, Map 11)

Green accounting has now been 'tested in dozens of countries and well established in a few' (Hecht, 1999, p. 14) and has proved useful. However, Robert Repetto (2007), whose study of Indonesia first identified the scale of distortion in not accounting for resource depletion in the SNA, has criticised the slow rate of progress in developing and standardising the methodology. Perhaps the problem is that the need for green accounts is greatest in southern countries, but northern countries tend to dominate international agendas.

Activity 3.8

Review Book 1, Chapter 3 and answer the following questions:

1 If GDP measures stem from mainstream neo-classical economics, what approach to economics fits with green accounting?

2 What steps in Lord Nicholas Stern's argument, succinctly set out in the answer to Activity 3.4, go beyond neo-classical approaches?

3 Which of the other approaches to economics identified by Graham Dawson might address Stern's concerns?

Green accounting, which supplements mainstream accounts by adding resource and pollution externalities, is consistent with Graham Dawson's account of environmental economics. Stern also took account of non-market impacts, concentration of harm in low-income countries and very long-term effects. Although not fully articulated in Graham Dawson's account, these kinds of issue are addressed by ecological economics.

6 Ecological economics

Ecological economics is based on a trenchant critique of mainstream economics, and is, as Graham Dawson mentioned 'a work in progress' rather than a fully developed approach. Malte Faber (2008) sums up this critique by asserting that mainstream economics lacks adequate concepts of nature, justice and time. In effect, he states, mainstream economics embodies an assumption that technological development and economic growth can overcome any resource shortage, by substituting alternative forms of capital, and will in the future provide for all at levels that make justice irrelevant and permit economists to discount future needs. The environment is reduced to a minor appendage of the economy and economics is able to present itself as a value free analysis of efficient conduct of the economy.

Ecological economics, on the contrary, assumes that the economy is embedded within the environment, indeed depends on natural capital and ecosystem services, some of which cannot, or should not, be substituted. Ecological economists have been concerned with the scale of the economy – how large it can become without overwhelming its own resource base – and accept that there must be a limit (Daly, 2003, pp. 16–18). This suggests that there could be limits to economic growth, and hence that questions of intra- and intergenerational justice cannot be ignored. Ecological economists seek to balance human dignity and the dignity of nature, and thus to provide an adequate quality of life to existing humans without compromising nature or future generations. They therefore support the idea of strong SD, with a particular focus on ecological sustainability. These considerations locate ecological economics firmly in the critical approach territory, as introduced in Chapter 1 of this book. Faber (2008) notes that in taking ecology, justice and time seriously, ecological economists face a much more complicated world than do mainstream economists. Inge Ropke (2005) adds that they have so far done more in thinking through the consequences of taking nature seriously than they have of social justice.

In practice, much of the work in ecological economics has focused on interdisciplinary work linking economics and ecology. Robert Costanza et al. (1991), for example, define ecological economics as concerned with all the interactions between economy and ecology, and contrast it with both conventional economics and conventional ecology. Since they are less optimistic about technology and growth than are conventional economists, they propose that the most prudent course is to maintain total natural capital stocks at or above their present level. This leads on to a huge amount of work in understanding natural ecosystems and seeking management principles which will provide for humans without compromising sustainability – including the work on resilience discussed above. In turn, as examined by Faber et al. (1996), this raises complex conceptual problems around the relationship between society and nature, including energy and material flows, evolution, the nature of science and the role of entropy. In their interpretation, ecological economics becomes very philosophical, and apparently far from the pressing problems and policy issues which pre-occupy this course.

For the concept of entropy see Book 1, Chapter 3

The focus on justice has been most consistently raised by one of the founders of the approach, Martinez-Alier. He not only wrote the first book entitled *Ecological Economics* (1987), tracing a variety of intellectual forebears, but has had a long-standing interest in the environmentalism of poor people and in the political ecology of the South. With an Indian colleague, Guha, he has directly challenged the argument that poverty is a cause of environmental degradation, instead insisting that northern consumption, linked to unfair terms of trade and controls on international migration, drives both poverty and environmental degradation in the countries of the South (Guha and Martinez-Alier, 1997, pp. 46–76). They argued (p. 91) that the world needs an environmental ethic that combines diversity, sustainability and equity. Accordingly, ecological economics has to deal with different values which cannot always be reduced to a single metric.

Herman Daly (2003, pp. 259–76) develops the concern with justice into a critique of one of the central claims of mainstream economics, still more of neoliberalism: the claim that markets are the ideal form of resource allocation and need no political intervention. He points out that markets balance supply and demand, but that demand depends on the existing distribution of property and income, which may result from a variety of historic processes, including conquest and theft as well as more reputable processes. Hence, there is no guarantee that the distribution of property and income are themselves either fair or efficient. He also points out that the concept of efficiency usually used by economists is Pareto efficiency, that is an allocation that makes everybody as well off as they can be without making anyone less well off. This definition excludes the possibility of redistribution, even if that redistribution would contribute to 'the greatest good for the greatest number'. Even though Daly accepts that markets are efficient, he insists that their efficiency does not address the question of fairness in the distribution of property and income, a question that is political rather than economic.

Ropke (2005) has traced the development of ecological economics since its institutionalisation in 1988, arguing that though it remains a heterogeneous movement with a range of interests and emphases, it has substantial achievements to its credit (one of which is the success of the idea of the ecological footprint, discussed several times in this course). She notes recurring debates about the relationship of economies to nature, with themes including energy flows, resource substitution, trade and economic growth, the scale of the economy, quality of life and values. Scanning the titles of papers in the journal *Ecological Economics*, it is clear that many of the empirical and conceptual papers are concerned with processes occurring in the South. Ropke argues that rather than being a weakness, the heterogeneity of approaches and the variety of debates, both internally and with related disciplines, is actually a strength, since it leaves no assumption unquestioned and contributes to conceptual clarification. Whether that clarification can be sufficient to allow ecological economics to provide the reconciliation of environmental and economic governance that this book seeks, remains to be seen. A first step would be to begin to shift the assumptions and practices of mainstream economics, but that is no easy task.

If the effects of decades of effort to develop ecological economics and green accounting, discussed in the previous section, are compared, considerable similarities appear. Even though green accounting tackles a limited problem – adding resource and ecosystem accounts to the SNA – while ecological economics mounts a broad critique of mainstream economics, progress in both is limited. Each has achieved significant success, but neither has made much progress in changing mainstream ideas and practices. Hence, both give indications of how economics and environment could be reconciled, and that such reconciliation would be especially helpful in the subsistence and resource exporting economies of the South. So far, neither has shifted the positions of the international institutions that keep mainstream economics, and especially its neoliberal variant, pre-eminent over equity and environment.

7 Conclusion

Relating the arguments and evidence presented in the chapter back to the Introduction and Learning outcomes, I believe I have shown that the conventional view of the South is indeed wrong both in its diagnosis and in its prescription. Looked at through the perspectives of political ecology and resilience, the South both provides examples of good practice and a challenge for the North.

From this point of view, most of the problems of the South result more from the way that it is incorporated in the international political economy than from the inadequacies of its societies. Indigenous groups often follow sustainable livelihoods and resist unjust and unsustainable developments. In spite of the pressures of the Washington Consensus and business interests, some southern governments have recognised that livelihoods depend on the environment and attempted to develop policies that will be ecologically and socially sustainable. Much remains to be done to think through and implement a process of development that will respect both environment and the poor, but southern societies and governments should be seen as potential contributors to the innovation process rather than just recipients.

The challenge to the North is to recognise that, rather than being role models the South should follow, it is a major cause of the South's problems. Northern societies should recognise their own dependence on the environment, adopt more sustainable livelihoods at home, and move to assisting, rather than exploiting, the South. Since current forms of economic decision making neglect environment and inequality, the principles of ecological economics should help to overcome this. However, those principles make clear that more sustainable and equitable practices will depend on politics as well as economics. Any radical transformation of the North will be actively resisted by beneficiaries of the current system and face apathy or worse from most northern citizens. Indeed, the conceptual and political problems of attempting to reconcile economy, environment and equity are so formidable that it is hard to avoid the conclusion that, however desirable, they are completely infeasible. Hence, it is reassuring that one group of northern countries has been engaged in exactly this task for decades, as explained in the next chapter.

Online Exercise 16

Now log on to the course website and complete Online Exercise 16: *Ecological restoration and green accounting*.

Video 6

Now watch Video 6: *Bangladesh: energy futures.*

References

Adger, W. (2000) 'Social and ecological resilience: are they related?', *Progress in Human Geography*, vol. 24, no. 3, pp. 347–64.

Bartelmus, P. (2008) 'Green accounting' [online], *Encyclopedia of Earth*, http://www.eoearth.org/article/Green_accounting (Accessed 14 October 2008).

Berkes, F. (1999) *Sacred Ecology: Traditional Ecological Knowledge and Resource Management*, Philadelphia, Taylor and Francis.

Bernstein, S. (2001) *The Compromise of Liberal Environmentalism*, New York, Columbia University Press.

Bryant, R. L. (2001) 'Political ecology: a critical agenda for change?' in Castree, N. and Braun, B. (eds) *Social Nature: Theory, Practice, and Politics*, Malden, MA, Oxford and Victoria, Blackwell Publishing, pp. 151–69.

Bryant, R. L. and Bailey, S. (1997) *Third World Political Ecology*, London, Routledge.

Castree, N. (2005) *Nature*, Abingdon, Routledge.

Costanza, R., Daly, H. E. and Bartholomew, J. A. (1991) 'Goals, agenda and policy recommendations for ecological economics' in Costanza, R. (ed) *Ecological Economics: The Science and Management of Sustainability*, New York, Columbia University Press.

Daly, H. with Farley, J. (2003) *Ecological Economics: Principles and Applications*, Washington, DC, Island Press.

Eder, K. (1996) *The Social Construction of Nature: A Sociology of Ecological Enlightenment*, London, Sage.

Faber, M. (2008) 'How to be an ecological economist', *Ecological Economics*, vol. 66, no. 1, pp. 1–7.

Faber, M., Manstetten, R. and Proops, J. (1996) *Ecological Economics. Concepts and Methods*, Cheltenham, Edward Elgar.

Fischer, J., Lindenmayer, D. and Manning, A. (2006) 'Biodiversity, ecosystem function and resilience: ten principles for commodity production landscapes', *Frontiers in Ecology and Environment*, vol. 4, no. 2, pp. 80–6.

Folke, C. et al. (2002) *Resilience and Sustainable Development: Building Adaptive Capacity in a World of Transformation*, Stockholm, Edita Norstedts, Tryckeri AB.

Food and Agricultural Organization (FAO) (1997) *Irrigation Potential in Africa* [online], FAO Land and Water Division, www.fao.org/docrep/W4347E/w4347e0i.jpg (Accessed 1 December 2008).

Forest Peoples' Programme (2008) *Sustainable Livelihoods* [online], http://www.forestpeoples.org/documents/sust_livehds/bases/sust_livelihoods.shtml (Accessed 14 October 2008).

Guha, R. (2000) *Environmentalism: A Global History,* New York, Longman.

Guha, R. and Martinez-Alier, J. (1997) *Varieties of Environmentalism: Essays North and South,* London, Earthscan.

Gunderson, L. (2000) 'Ecological resilience in theory and practice', *Annual Review of Ecology and Systematics,* vol. 31, pp. 425–39.

Hardin, G. (1968) 'The tragedy of the commons', *Science,* no. 162, pp. 1243–48.

Hecht, J. E. (1999) 'Environmental accounting: where we are now, where we are heading', *Resources,* no. 135, pp. 14–17.

Holling, C. (1973) 'Resilience and stability of ecological systems', *Annual Review of Ecology and Systematics,* vol. 4, pp. 1–23.

IDRC (International Development Research Centre) (1998) *Tapping into Fog* [online], IDRC, Ottawa, Canada, www.idrc.ca/en/ev-26965-201-1-DO_TOPIC.html (Accessed 30 March 2009).

Lange, G. M., Hassan, R. and Hamilton, K. (2003) *Environmental Accounting in Action. Case Studies from Southern Africa,* Cheltenham, Edward Elgar.

Lange, G. M., Mungatana, E. and Hassan, R. (2007) 'Water accounting for the Orange River Basin: An economic perspective on managing a transboundary resource', *Ecological Economics,* vol. 61, no. 4, pp. 660–70.

Marten, G. G. (2001) *Human Ecology, Basic Concepts for Sustainable Development,* London, Earthscan.

Martinez-Alier, J. (1987) *Ecological Economics: Energy, Environment and Society,* Oxford, Blackwell.

Martinez-Alier, J. (2002) *The Environmentalism of the Poor,* Cheltenham, Edward Elgar.

Peterson, G., Allen, C. and Holling, C. (1998) 'Ecological resilience, biodiversity and scale', *Ecosystems,* vol. 1, pp. 6–18.

Rangachari, R., Sengupta, N., Iyer, R. R., Banerji, P. and Singh, S. (2000) *Large Dams: India's Experience* [online], a WCD case study prepared as an input to the World Commission on Dams, Cape Town, www.dams.org/kbase/studies/in (Accessed 14 February 2009).

Repetto, R. (2007) 'Comments on environmental accounting', *Ecological Economics*, vol. 61, no. 4, pp. 611–12.

Robbins, P. (2003) 'Political ecology in political geography', *Political Geography*, vol. 22, no. 6, pp. 641–45.

Ropke, I. (2005) 'Trends in the development of environmental economics from the late 1980s to the early 2000s', *Environmental Economics*, vol. 55, no. 2, pp. 262–90.

Saiko, T. (2001) *Environmental Crises: Geographical Case Studies in Post-socialist Eurasia*, Harlow, Pearson Education.

Shaxon, N. (2007) *Poisoned Wells: The Dirty Politics of African Oil*, New York, Palgrave Macmillan.

Shiva, V. (1994) *Staying Alive. Women, Ecology and Development*, London, Zed Books.

Steinberg, P. (2001) *Environmental Leadership in Developing Countries: Transnational Relations and Biodiversity Policy in Costa Rica and Bolivia*, Cambridge, MA, and London, MIT Press.

Swanson, P. (2001) *Water: the Drop of Life*, companion to the public television series, Minnetonka, MN, North Word Press.

United Nations (UN), European Commission, International Monetary Fund (IMF), Organisation for Economic Co-operation and Development (OECD) and World Bank (2003) *Handbook for Integrated Environmental and Economic Accounting* [online], New York, UN Statistical Division, http://unstats.un.org/unsd/envaccounting/seea.asp (Accessed 1 December 2008).

Wapner, P. (2003) 'World Summit on Sustainable Development: toward a post Jo'burg environmentalism', *Global Environmental Politics*, vol. 3, no. 1, pp. 1–10.

Chapter 4

Look North: environmental responses in consumer democracies – the case of the European Union

Petr Jehlička

Contents

1 Introduction

For the sake of simplicity, in this chapter I use the 'EU' for the whole period of European integration. Using this shorthand conceals changes in the size of the Union, in its institutions and in the 'depth' of integration.

When the course team considered what would be the best example of an innovation in environmental governance in the developed world, there was one outstanding candidate. What is now the European Union (EU) is the result of a unique experiment in international collaboration that has transformed Europe from a continent of simmering international tensions, with frequent major wars, into a community where tensions are managed through negotiation. An initial concern with peace and security after 1945 has evolved through a number of stages, starting with the inception of the European Coal and Steel Community in 1951, progressing via the Treaty of Rome in 1957, through the 'common market' and the European Community to the European Union, created by the Maastricht Treaty of 1992. Starting from a nucleus of six countries, it has also expanded to its current total of 27, with others eager to join. Throughout the process, there has been intense debate about what the EU is for, whether its role should be mainly economic or also political and military, what powers should be left with nation states and what needs to be harmonised and dealt with at supranational level. Within the broad debate, the EU has become a leader in national and international environmental policy making, including a pioneer role in developing policy for sustainable consumption (SC). This unit asks what we can learn from the strengths and weaknesses of the EU as an environmental policy actor. I start with an upbeat assessment from the USA.

Activity 4.1

Read the article below and draw up a list of the claims it makes about the EU as an environmental policy actor.

Will the Environmentalists Find Their Voice?

Once an environmental leader, U.S. now barely follows

... For three decades, the United States was the world's environmental trendsetter. But now leadership comes from the European Union, a phenomenon I observed firsthand last spring as a Fulbright scholar teaching comparative environmental law at the University of Ljubljana in Slovenia.

The most prominent example is global warming. Despite a strong scientific consensus that Earth's temperatures are rising because of human activity, the Bush administration clings stubbornly to its opposition to mandatory limits on greenhouse gases ... Meanwhile, in 2005 the EU embarked on an aggressive approach to limiting greenhouse gases, modeled after market-based strategies to controlling acid-rain emissions pioneered by the United States. ....

The EU also is on the verge of adopting a 'chemicals policy' embodying the principle of precaution – a 'better safe than sorry' approach. In both the United States and Europe, thousands of chemicals are used in commerce, even though we know very little about their potential toxic impacts. Under current regulation, chemical producers rarely are required to test chemicals before using them; instead, the government must demonstrate a toxin is unsafe to halt its use. The EU's new policy shifts the burden of proof. Before chemicals that raise significant health concerns may be used, producers will have to show, through testing if necessary, that the chemical is safe, or that the benefits of its use outweigh the risks, including that there are no available substitutes. ...

Additionally, the EU is leading the way in innovative recycling practices, including laws requiring producers to 'take back' products from consumers at the end of their useful life and to pay for their recycling and disposal. In this way, the price of these products will reflect the true costs they impose on the environment. Under recent EU directives, consumers can now return computers, electronic equipment and automobiles at the end of their useful life free of charge to certified collection centers. The United States has no comparable system, although in 2003, California imposed a fee on electronics purchases to fund recycling facilities.

The EU is outpacing the United States with incentives for market-based environmental strategies, including promoting a reliable market for Earth-friendly products. Unlike the United States, where 'green' consumers must sift through a confusing array of labels and advertising claims, in Europe, certifying boards determine whether products meet environmental goals. Consumers in Europe can shop for green appliances, cleaning and paper products, home and garden supplies, lubricants, clothing and tourist services. Likewise, large companies in the EU are expected to disclose to investors and the public far more detailed information about the environmental impact of their activities – a boost to the socially responsible investment movement.

The record is not one-sided. Our Endangered Species Act, although now under attack, has more teeth than comparable EU laws. The EU has no equivalent to the federal Environmental Protection Agency's Superfund program, despite its thousands of contaminated waste sites. And the culture of strong environmental enforcement is still only taking root in many EU countries.

> On balance, however, the EU is tackling its most pressing environmental problems with a focus and creativity Americans can only envy. ... we should learn from the EU's innovative approaches. (Indeed, California's recent electronic waste law and ban on flame retardants were modeled in part after Europe's system.) By doing so, we can reassert our role as the world's environmental leader.
>
> Cliff Rechtschaffen is a member scholar of the Center for Progressive Reform and a professor of law at Golden Gate University School of Law in San Francisco.
>
> (Rechtschaffen, 2006)

Apart from EU international leadership on climate change, my list of the claims made in the article includes the EU's takeover of global environmental leadership from the USA (the EU's external role), its internal resolve to force the chemical industry to prove their products' harmlessness to human health (and thus to protect EU citizens and consumers) and the provision of information on products' environmental impacts. Clifford Rechtschaffen's article thus contains a number of pointers to the two major themes I will address in this chapter: EU environmental leadership and the challenge of consumption governance. It is of note that this favourable assessment of EU environmental policy was written by a US scholar who was familiar with both the US and EU approaches to the environment. Nonetheless, in the rest of this chapter some of the claims in the article will be subjected to critical examination.

As SC is one of the areas in which the EU proclaims its ambitions for global environmental leadership and, as you have seen in Rechtschaffen's introductory article, these ambitions are increasingly externally recognised, it is important to subject these claims to critical scrutiny. More specifically, I will consider how SC promoted by the EU helps set consumption patterns in the North at levels to which the South can aspire (*course theme 4*). Thus, in keeping with the focus of Book 3 on *course question 4*, you will a) examine the extent to which the EU's SC governance promotes the reduction in consumption levels in affluent societies and b) search both in the text of the chapter and online for existing social phenomena that in the EU context constitute low consumption practices. I will be also looking at the transfer of SC governance in the context of eastern enlargement of the EU, which will enable me to engage with *course theme 2*.

However, to assess the EU's approach to SC, which is addressed in Section 4, I need to start this chapter by exploring the development of the EU's approach to environmental policy. I will begin this chapter by looking at the question of how the EU gained internal competences and the power to act externally in the field of environmental policy, to which the 1957 Treaty of Rome contained no reference (Section 2). I will explain how, by the end of the last century, there were approximately 300 pieces of environmentally related legislation binding on member states. You will also learn in Section 2 how by the early 2000s the EU had become a party to some 60 international environmental agreements. These findings will feed into the subsequent discussion in Section 3 on how the form of the EU's environmental management (*course question 2*) relates to the promotion of sustainable development (SD), of which the EU became the leading international advocate.

1.1 Learning outcomes

This chapter should enable you to:

- develop your understanding of the emergence of the EU as a powerful and innovative actor in international environmental politics
- critically analyse the variant of SD practised by the EU, including its concept of SC
- critically assess the extent to which the EU offers a model of international and supranational environmental management and cooperation.

2 The emergence of the European Union as an environmental policy actor

In the Introduction, I highlighted the EU's active participation (and often leadership) in international environmental agreements and the large body of internal environmental legislation. In this section, I will explain how the EU developed internal competence in environmental policy even though this was not among its original aims.

The initiatives that eventually institutionalised the process of European integration in the 1950s were initially focused on utilising the military and economic potential of West Germany for the benefit of the West in its competition with the Soviet bloc, while allaying the concerns of Germany's neighbour France (Dinan, 2008). Binding Germany and its strategic steel and coal resources into a broader European initiative joined by the three Benelux countries and Italy was also an opportunity to advance the more idealistic goal of European cooperation and unity. This was the rationale for the launch in 1952 (the Treaty of Paris was signed a year earlier) of the European Coal and Steel Community, with the seat of its 'high authority' in Luxembourg. Its architect was a senior French civil servant, Jean Monnet. A more ambitious attempt to extend the integration process to the sensitive area of defence – the European Defence Community – was negotiated in the mid 1950s but never implemented because the treaty was not ratified by the French parliament.

Supranationalism refers to processes in which decisions are made by institutions which are largely independent of national governments, i.e. processes above states.

From the start the process of European integration was for the pursuit of national strategic interests through the establishment of **supranational** institutions (that is institutions acting above the level of states), combined with more idealistic goals of European unity as an agent of world peace, cooperation and well-being. This was the case with the next integration initiative, which led to the signing of the Treaty of Rome on the European Economic Community in 1957 and its launch in 1958. The primary aim of the same six founding member states formulated in the treaty was to establish an internal common market in which goods, people, services and capital could move freely as a means for achieving greater prosperity.

The Treaty of Rome established three of the main institutions of the EU, though you should see neither the institutions themselves nor the relations between them as fixed. Their internal set-up, roles and the power relations among them are evolving as the process of integration progresses. For example, the predecessor of the directly elected parliament was an assembly of appointed members. Also, the rise in importance and weight of the European Parliament circumscribed the

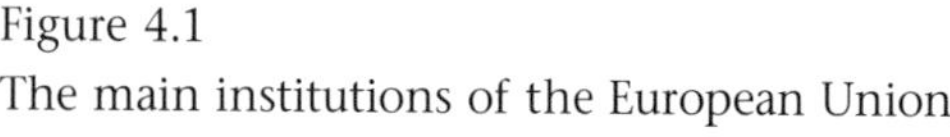

Figure 4.1
The main institutions of the European Union

Council of Ministers' ability to impose its views, and the growing agenda-setting power of the European Council impinged on the European Commission's right of initiative. The five main institutions (Figure 4.1), in their 2008 form, are introduced in Box 4.1.

Box 4.1 Institutions of the European Union

The European Commission is both the executive body – the College of Commissioners (in 2008 there were twenty-seven commissioners, one appointed by each member state) – and the administrative body (the bureaucracy), consisting of over twenty directorates-general (DGs). DGs are the equivalents of national ministries. The Commission is charged with initiating policies and representing the general interest of the EU; acting as guardian of the treaties; ensuring the correct application of EU legislation; and managing and negotiating international trade and cooperation agreements. Fewer than 25,000 civil servants are employed in the administrative body, equivalent to the staff of a large local authority such as Barcelona.

The Council of Ministers (formally, the Council of the European Union) is the EU's primary decision-making body. Each member state is represented by a minister. There are nine configurations of the council, which are determined by the policy area that is discussed. Each policy area determines the number of meetings, which ranges from one to twelve a year. Its main job is to agree legislation proposed by the Commission. The treaties allow for three ways of voting in the council: unanimity, simple majority and qualified majority voting (QMV). Over three-quarters of all EU legislation is agreed by QMV. Under the Nice Treaty, QMV means 255 votes out of 345 in the Council of Ministers, i.e. 74 per cent (each country is allocated a number of votes approximately proportional to its population – the UK has twenty-nine votes and Malta has three votes), a majority of member states as well as 62 per cent of the EU's population. The Council *presidency* is held by a member state for six months. The presidency arranges and chairs all meetings of the Council and has responsibility for coordinating the EU's foreign policy.

The European Parliament is the only directly elected EU institution. Starting with the 2009 European election, it will have 750 MEPs. It has supervisory, legislative and budgetary powers. It appoints the whole Commission by a vote of confidence and has the right to sack the whole Commission. The Parliament has the right of co-decision – a procedure under which the newly proposed legislation has to be approved by both the Commission and the

Parliament (some sensitive areas such as taxation and agriculture still remained exempt in 2008).

The European Council (of Heads of State and Government) started in the 1970s as a series of informal meetings (often referred to in the media as 'European Summits') of the member states' heads of state and government. It was granted legal status by the first revision of the Treaty of Rome – the 1986 Single European Act (SEA) – and assigned responsibility for general political direction for the EU by the second amendment of the treaty – the 1992 Maastricht Treaty.

The task of the **European Court of Justice** is to ensure that the law is observed in the interpretation and application of the treaties. It adjudicates disputes among EU institutions and between EU institutions and member states. It also ensures national compliance with treaties. A number of the Court's decisions accelerated the process of integration. In 1963, the court established that citizens of EU member states had a right to expect their governments to adhere to their European obligations. A year later, the court established the supremacy of EU law.

Source: Bomberg and Stubb, 2008, pp. 46–64

2.1 Environmental competence at the Union level

Although the Treaty of Rome was primarily focused on agriculture and trade, through the setting up of the Common Agricultural Policy and the common market, it also included enabling clauses which allowed other issues to be taken to the supranational level. Some of these were to facilitate the common market, others reflected broader objectives. Article 100 of the treaty authorised the Council of Ministers to issue directives for the promotion of the proper functioning of the common market. Article 235 accorded the Council the authority to add new objectives to complement the market (Hildebrand, 2005, p. 23). Article 2 expressed the broader goals, since it called for the promotion of harmonious development of economic activities, a continuous and balanced expansion, an increase in stability, an accelerated raising of the *standard of living* and closer relations between the states belonging to the EU (Hildebrand, 2005, p. 22). The European Commission in particular tended to interpret this mandate both as an improved *standard of living* and an *improved quality of life*, invoking the more idealistic goals of European integration and implying that environmental protection might be one of the EU's objectives. For the Commission, as an institution representing the interests of the EU as whole, environmental protection became an attractive policy area as it offered an opportunity

Different types of EU secondary legislation were introduced as 'EU secondary environmental legislation' in Book 2, Chapter 8. EU primary legislation is the treaties.

for the EU to have a policy reach which had not been included in the treaty (Sbragia, 2005, p. 204).

In 1968, the Commission, influenced by the growing environmental movement and concerned with national regulations posing **non-tariff barriers** (that is barriers to trade other than tariffs) to the functioning of the common market, proposed a programme of harmonisation of these regulations, including the regulations in the field of environmental protection, which was then under the exclusive jurisdiction of member states. To keep the playing field level the Commission began to introduce Union-wide, common environmental legislation. EU environmental legislation was initially related to the better functioning of the common market.

Non-tariff barriers are national standards (for example, health regulations) that have an effect equivalent to tariffs by deterring imports.

These developments were in line with one perspective of European integration – the so-called Monnet method of integration. Monnet believed that integration had to be achieved by small, incremental steps that would address 'technical' issues first. These steps would be taken in economic sectors, including agriculture, where they would not impinge on national sovereignty rather than in the 'high politics' of defence and external relations. According to Monnet, the Union should initially strive for limited achievements that would lead to de facto solidarity defined in terms of emerging common interests. The idea that economic integration would produce political integration via the so-called spillover effect was at the core of an early theory of European integration called **neofunctionalism** (Haas, 1964). The roots of this way of thinking lie in functionalism, formulated by David Mitrany in the 1930s. In contrast to neofunctionalism's emphasis on regional integration of states such as the EU, functionalism was concerned with international integration in which the authority was linked with functions and needs rather than territories.

Neofunctionalism is a theory of European integration which claims that economic integration ultimately leads to political integration.

The surge of public concern about environmental protection in the late 1960s and early 1970s and the United Nations (UN) Stockholm Conference on the Human Environment had a strong influence on the emergence of EU environmental competence. The 1972 meeting of the European Council marked the origin of the process of formalisation and institutionalisation of environmental policy as a distinct policy sector at the supranational – EU – level.

The Stockholm conference was discussed in Book 2, Chapters 7 and 9

The meeting issued a declaration calling upon EU institutions to prepare an action programme on the environment. This first Environmental Action Programme (EAP) covered the period from 1973 to 1976. Although it was a legally non-binding document, it provided a framework and strategic direction for the development of the content of EU environmental policy. Several long-term principles of EU

The **prevention principle** refers to taking action before the damage occurs. In contrast to the precautionary principle (introduced in Book 1, Chapter 1), the prevention principle refers to tackling risks under certainty.

The polluter pays principle was introduced in Book 2, Chapter 8

environmental policy were formulated in the first EAP including the **prevention principle**, which requires taking action before damage occurs, and the polluter pays principle. For the first time, the Commission declared in the first EAP that economic growth was not an end in itself and that reducing disparities in living conditions between members should be a primary EU objective (Weale et al., 2000, p. 56). Between 1977 and the late 2000s five more EAPs were adopted. They provided frameworks within which secondary legislation such as directives and regulations was developed and funding priorities in the field of environmental protection were determined.

2.2 The Europeanisation of member states' environmental policies

Europeanisation is the process in which national institutions and policies adapt to EU policies while also themselves influencing policies and institutions at the EU level.

New points of leverage can be, for example, the distribution of funding – via various national or international intermediaries – to domestic environmental non-governmental organisations (NGOs) or by making access to EU pre-accession funds contingent on including NGOs in the domestic bodies making a decision on their disbursement.

The EU also has a profound influence internally – on the domestic policies of its member states, including environmental policy. Since the 1990s, the exploration of the convergence of national environmental policies as a result of supranational influence has been conducted under the '**Europeanisation**' school of thought (Jordan and Liefferink, 2004a). A major comparative analysis of the Europeanisation of environmental policies in nine member states of the EU (Jordan and Liefferink, 2004b) conducted before the 2004 and 2007 enlargements of the EU (ten and two new member states respectively) found that since 1972 the EU had had a significant effect on the content of national policies. The Europeanisation of environmental policy had the most profound effect in the area of pollution regulations covering quality standards and requiring particular technologies and processes.

Christopher Knill (2001, pp. 214–15) argued that the EU had a top-down impact on member states in the following three ways:

- It prescribed clear models of national action, usually in the form of directives and regulations.
- It altered domestic political opportunity structures by offering national actors new points of leverage to achieve domestic change.
- It affected national beliefs and perceptions indirectly through the publication of strategies, informal **benchmarking** exercises and research.

In this context, **benchmarking** is the use of comparisons with other member states with the aim of learning from their experience to improve performance.

In reality, EU environmental policy is made in a more reciprocal and complex way than suggested by this one-way, top-down model. Europeanisation can be understood as a dynamic that involves a top-down process of the enactment and implementation of EU environmental directives and a bottom–up process, which involves not just adoption but the adaptation of EU legislation and policy to the national context. There is also an upward oriented influence – sometimes called 'domestication' of EU policy (Jordan and Liefferink, 2004a, p. 21) – of members states on the EU level. 'Leader' states often seek to export their domestic approaches to the European level with the aim of reducing adjustment costs and legal and political uncertainty.

However, most of the countries under investigation (seven out of nine) were members of the EU during the whole period and could, therefore, influence the formulation of EU environmental policy that would ultimately affect them. In contrast, the twelve countries that joined the EU in two waves in 2004 and 2007, most of which were former state-socialist countries in central-eastern and south-eastern Europe, experienced Europeanisation of their national environmental policies (as well as of other policy areas) in a strictly top-down manner that would be a perfect fit with Knill's analytical model. Joanne Caddy (1997) described the process of speedy adoption of some 300 pieces of EU environmental legislation by these candidate countries as 'hierarchical imposition'. Susan Baker and Ian Welsh (2000) also criticised its undemocratic character and contrasted it with previously positive impacts of environmental policy on legitimacy and governance both in the EU and candidate countries for membership. Nonetheless, in practice, Europeanisation of environmental policy in these countries was applauded by both EU and domestic actors as an unqualified success.

Activity 4.2

This is your first opportunity to engage with the third learning outcome of this chapter – to assess the extent to which the EU offers a model of international and supranational environmental management and cooperation. Why do you think that the adoption of the EU model of environmental policy by the 2004 and 2007 accession states was seen in such a positive light?

One reason was that the former state-socialist countries suffered from severe industrial pollution, to which the EU model of environmental management provided an effective response. The adoption of EU environmental legislation (as part of the whole package of rights and obligations derived from the EU treaties, laws and court rulings, known as the **acquis communautaire**) was therefore perceived as a major step forward because of its contribution to the clean-up of industrial pollution and the modernising of environmental governance. In addition, the adoption of EU environmental governance was also credited with raising the profile of environmental protection at a time when economic considerations became the national governments' overriding priority. However, as preparations for membership were

The rights and obligations derived from the EU treaties, laws and court rulings are referred to as **acquis communautaire**.

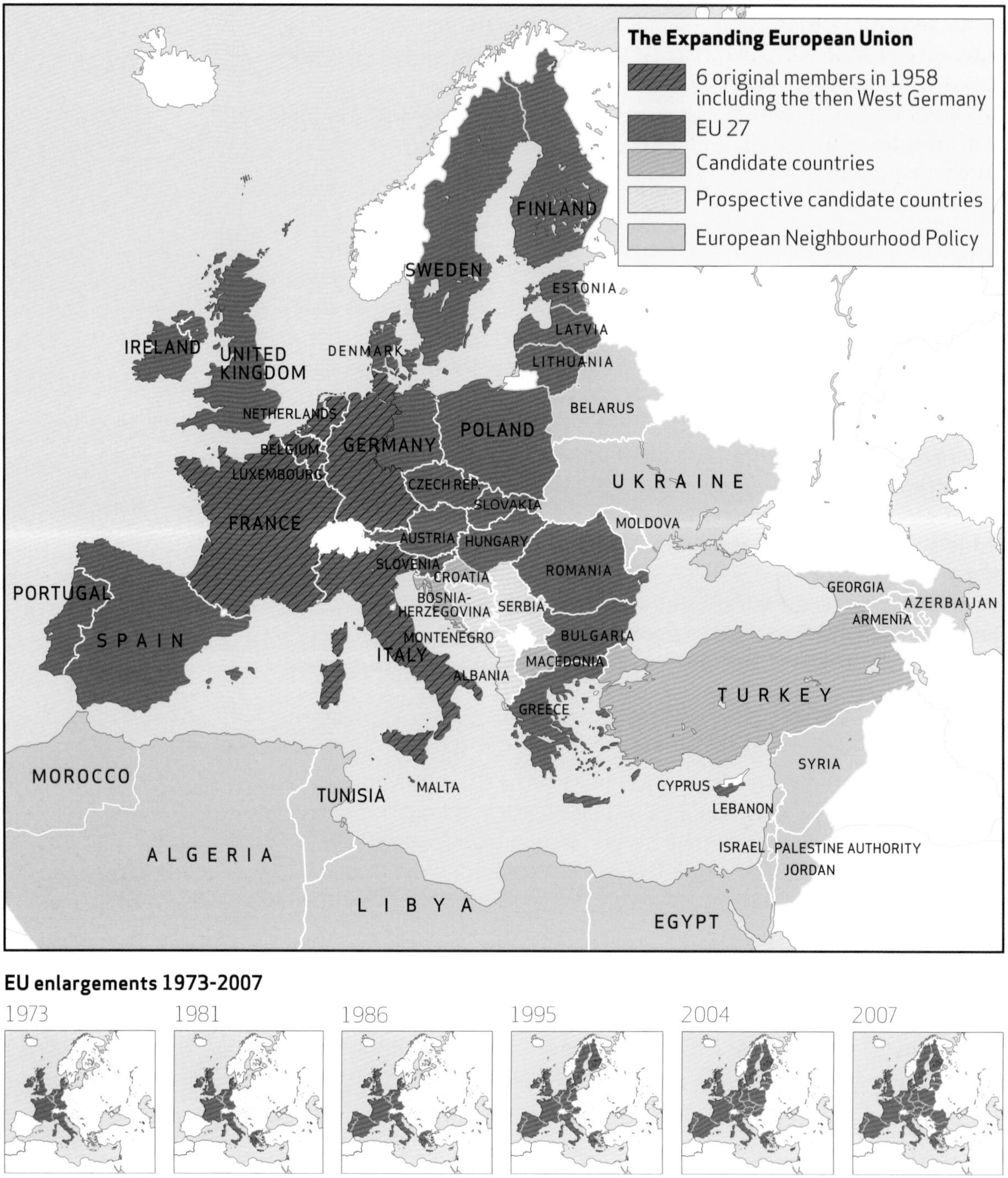

The Expanding European Union

6 original members in 1958 including the then West Germany
EU 27
Candidate countries
Prospective candidate countries
European Neighbourhood Policy

FINLAND
SWEDEN
ESTONIA
LATVIA
LITHUANIA
IRELAND
UNITED KINGDOM
DENMARK
NETHERLANDS
BELGIUM
LUXEMBOURG
GERMANY
POLAND
BELARUS
CZECH REP.
SLOVAKIA
UKRAINE
FRANCE
AUSTRIA
HUNGARY
MOLDOVA
SLOVENIA
CROATIA
ROMANIA
PORTUGAL
SPAIN
BOSNIA-HERZEGOVINA
SERBIA
MONTENEGRO
ITALY
BULGARIA
GEORGIA
AZERBAIJAN
ARMENIA
MACEDONIA
ALBANIA
GREECE
TURKEY
MOROCCO
TUNISIA
MALTA
CYPRUS
SYRIA
LEBANON
ISRAEL
PALESTINE AUTHORITY
JORDAN
ALGERIA
LIBYA
EGYPT

EU enlargements 1973-2007

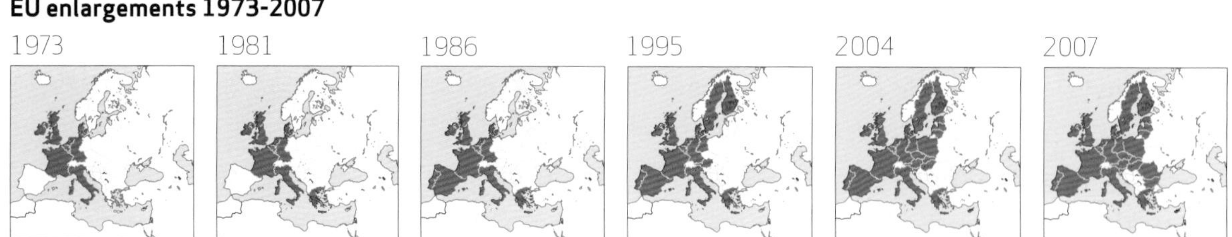

Figure 4.2
The expanding European Union, 1958–2007

perceived in terms of candidate countries catching up with the more advanced practices of their West European neighbours (Baker, 2006a, p. 207), no attempt was made to consider some East European practices and policies which had a strong degree of compatibility with the principles of SD – in particular SC practices such as integrated public transport, and waste management schemes such as returnable bottles – for policy transfer in the opposite direction (Jehlička and Tickle, 2004). I will return to this theme in greater detail in Section 4.

Historically, starting with the 1973 accession of the UK and Ireland to the EU, enlargements of the Union were driven by the candidate countries' desire to join. The EU has never invited others to join its club (Avery, 2008, p. 184). The appeal of the EU reaches far beyond the new member states in central-eastern and south-eastern Europe. Sixteen countries to the east and south of the current EU, including Ukraine, Armenia, Syria, Israel and Morocco, are developing political and economic links with the EU under the auspices of the European Neighbourhood Policy (see Figure 4.2). With each of these countries, the EU negotiated an action plan that covers a range of topics including economic and social reforms, trade, cooperation in justice and security affairs, transport, energy, environment and education (Avery, 2008). They require these countries to adopt EU regulation and a large part of the *acquis communautaire*, so the EU's internal arrangements are having very substantial international effects in its 'neighbourhood'.

2.3 The internationalisation of the European Union's environmental competence

With the development of internal environmental policies, the proliferation of international environmental agreements to which member states became parties, and with the associated fears of trade barriers arising from national implementation of these agreements, the case for the Commission's involvement in external relations in the field of the environment became more compelling.

The starting point was a 1971 ruling of the European Court of Justice. The court ruled that if the EU had been given the power to legislate internally for the EU, it implicitly had been given powers to act externally as well (Sbragia, 2005, p. 205). The ruling, along with the decision of the heads of governments of the member states to include the environment in the EU's portfolio of competences, enabled the Union's participation in international environmental politics. However, the court decision did not change the international status of member states, which remained subjects of international law. As a result,

Mixed competence areas were introduced in Book 2, Chapter 7

environmental policy became a mixed competence area (as distinct from the common trade, agricultural and fisheries policies in which the EU had exclusive competence).

The EU has not always been the international environmental leader as described in Rechtschaffen's introductory article. A significant transformation in international environmental politics occurred in the mid 1980s. In Book 2, Chapter 7 you learnt how the EU's position in ozone negotiations changed from being a foot dragger to a proponent of the Montreal Protocol. This period of intensive ozone diplomacy is sometimes associated with the beginning of the decline in the USA's international environmental leadership. With the ensuing shift of emphasis from ozone layer protection towards climate change, the EU replaced the USA as a leader of global environmental politics (Sbragia and Damro, 1999; Vogel, 2005; Zito, 2005). The 1986 SEA confirmed these developments by incorporating environmental competence into the treaty and both the SEA and the subsequent 1992 Maastricht Treaty on the European Union confirmed the EU's competence to conclude international environmental agreements.

Activity 4.3

How in your view might this change of leadership be explained?

It is clear that the USA retains the potential to exert a leadership role in any field, based on its political, economic and military power. The EU has certainly narrowed the economic gap as it has expanded, but remains far behind the USA in military power, and in most fields less effective politically. So, for the EU to overtake the USA as an international environmental leader, it requires the USA not to use its potential and the EU to perform unusually effectively.

It now seems that policy debates about SD and climate change are at variance with US values, which have increasingly reflected neoliberal preferences for markets over state intervention and, since 2001, for security issues. Perhaps because of half a century of unchallenged power, the USA is also more accustomed to pursuit of its own interests, if necessarily expressed unilaterally. The EU has been more inclined to temper the pursuit of economic growth with concerns about the environment and equity, and is well accustomed to the practice of international collaboration. Hence, environmental policy has been more consistent with EU values, especially as expressed in the language of SD.

3 Towards a sustainable European Union?

As I showed in the previous section, the initial driver for the development of the EU's internal environmental competence was the desire to avoid market distortions caused by the lack of harmonisation of environmental regulations. These measures were largely aimed at pollution control in member states. Such a development was therefore in keeping with the principal objective of the Treaty of Rome – the creation of the common market as a means for achieving prosperity. However, since the early 1990s the EU has placed strong emphasis on SD, perhaps reflecting the more idealistic motives for European integration. SD is now an objective of the EU, and environmental protection is now seen as an aim of integration. In this section, therefore, I will critically examine the emergence of the strong commitment of the EU to SD.

3.1 The European Union's commitment to sustainable development

The beginning of the Union's commitment to SD dates to the time of the publication of the 1987 Brundtland Report. Nonetheless, it was during and after the UN Conference on Environment and Development (UNCED) held in Rio de Janeiro in 1992 that the EU became a vigorous promoter of SD, both internally and externally. The internal dimension – embedding principles of SD in EU environmental policy – was manifest in a number of documents. The EU's role in environmental protection was first formally recognised in the 1986 SEA. Each subsequent amendment to the Treaty of Rome, starting with the 1992 Maastricht Treaty, articulated the EU's commitment to SD – a remarkable transformation for an organisation whose founding treaty was silent on the issue of the environment. The third modification of the treaty, the 1997 Amsterdam Treaty, declared economic and social progress and SD as official objectives of the EU. The 2001 Treaty of Nice, adopted mainly in preparation for the Union's eastern enlargements in 2004 and 2007, reaffirmed the status of SD in the EU.

UNCED was discussed in Book 2, Chapters 7, 8 and 9 and the Brundtland Commission that produced the report was introduced in Book 1, Chapter 1

The two EAPs adopted since 1992 – the fifth EAP *Towards Sustainability* (1992–2000) and the sixth EAP *Environment 2010: Our Future, Our Choice* (2001–10) (Figure 4.3) – also made strong declaratory commitments to the principle of SD. Unlike its predecessors, which addressed specific environmental problems, the fifth EAP – inspired by the Dutch National Environmental Policy Plan, which in turn was

Figure 4.3
Cover image of the sixth EU Environment Action Programme

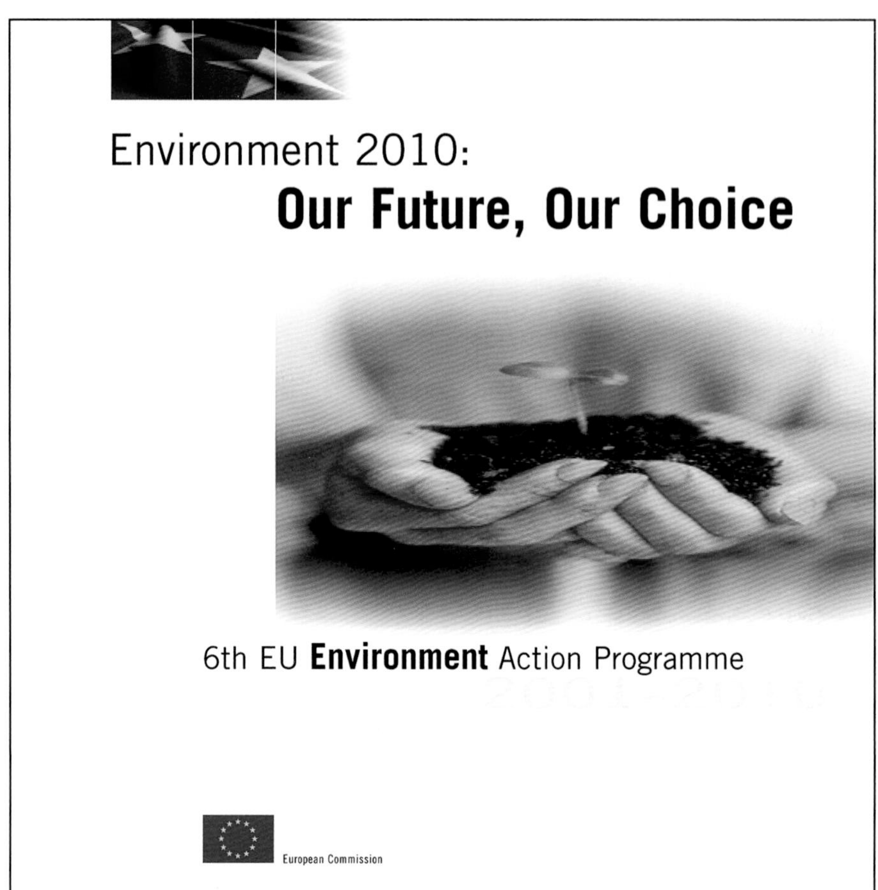

influenced by the Bruntdland Report – revolved around themes such as shared responsibility and partnership. Box 4.3 provides a summary of EU understanding of SD.

In principle, **environmental policy integration** (EPI) means the integration of environmental considerations in the design and implementation of policy.

Both the fifth and sixth EAPs declared strong commitments to **environmental policy integration** (EPI) as one of the key tools for policy delivery. The so-called Cardiff Process initiated by the Swedish prime minister and launched in 1998 is the principal strategy by which EPI is promoted at the EU level. Nine configurations of the European Council (meetings of ministers from member states, for example, the industry council, the agriculture council, the transport council, etc.) were called upon to develop EPI strategies and monitor and report progress (Baker, 2006a, p. 149).

Box 4.2 EU understanding of sustainable development

'Promoting SD is strongly linked with the stimulation of economic growth.' The conflict apparent in the pursuit of both environmental protection and economic growth is resolved by the idea of **decoupling** by increased eco-efficiency.

'The promotion of SD is primarily a cross-sectoral policy task.'

'The promotion of SD is a shared responsibility.' This is partly due to the EU having a system of multilevel governance. This characteristic is also related to SD as an ongoing process of stimulating behavioural and normative changes. Social and economic actors are expected to acknowledge the environmental consequences of their behaviour and to modify their actions.

'SD has social dimensions and is linked with issues of health and safety.' This is a specific reflection of the strong emphasis European political culture places on social concerns.

'Promoting SD is linked with the resolution of global environmental problems', in particular climate change and biodiversity.

'Promoting SD is a moral obligation.' The Commission has both recognised that European economic development has contributed to the global environmental crisis and has a capacity to lead the way in resolving that crisis.

Source: Baker, 2006a, pp. 145–7

Decoupling refers to breaking the link between environmental damage and economic growth. It is closely related to the idea of the Environmental Kuznets's Curve introduced in Book 2, Chapter 2.

Externally, there were serious attempts by the Union to engage with the Rio process leading up to and beyond the UN World Summit on Sustainable Development (WSSD) held in Johannesburg in 2002 (Vogler, 2005). In preparation for the WSSD, in 2001 the Commission formulated its strategy for the promotion of SD globally under the title 'A Sustainable Europe for a Better World: A European Union Strategy for Sustainable Development', which drew links between SD and ethical issues of justice, equity and democracy (Baker, 2007). In the same year, the Commission, at the request of the Council of Ministers, instituted Sustainability Impact Assessments as a means of integrating environmental considerations in all new trade agreements (Vogler, 2005).

So, from the early 1990s, the EU made a strong and consistent effort, both internally and externally, to promote SD. Indeed, as Baker and

John McCormick (2004) pointed out, because of the modifications of treaties, there is probably no single government or other association of states with such a strong constitutional commitment to SD as the EU. SD is now a norm of EU politics, both domestically and internationally. The EU seeks to promote SD beyond Europe through its enlargement, development, trade, environmental and foreign policies (Manners, 2006).

Activity 4.4

Why did SD become such an attractive concept for the EU, and why did environmental policy become increasingly couched in the language of SD?

To answer this question requires going beyond structural, procedural and material explanations for European integration. These explanations offered valuable insights into the rise of environmental policy as a consequence of the construction of the common market in a relatively small union. However, with the EU's growing diversity in the 1980s (after the accession of Greece in 1981 and Spain and Portugal in 1986) there emerged a greater need for an EU identity expressed through common values and goals that would provide legitimacy to the project of European integration. In particular since the Maastricht Treaty, EU central institutions have felt the need to mobilise popular support for the integration project (Baker, 2006b, p. 78).

The idea of SD had a lot to offer as a legitimising and mobilising value for European integration. Baker (2007) argued that the three-pillar focus of SD on the social, economic and ecological dimensions of development conformed to deep-seated European social constructs. While the European project was based on a belief in the achievement of economic prosperity through the creation of a common market, integration also had its roots in a belief in an ethos of collective societal responsibility for the welfare of the community as a whole (Baker, 2007). In addition, the idea of European integration and the concept of SD have in common an emphasis on enhancing participation and sharing responsibility.

Apart from its capacity to make the EU an institution more appealing to its citizens, SD offered an opportunity for the EU to develop its distinct international identity, a need felt particularly strongly in relation to the USA. The Union wanted to be seen as aligning with international best practice and as an advocate of North–South cooperation (Vogler, 2005). These claims are evident in the following quote from the *Review of the*

Sustainable Development Strategy (Council of the European Union, 2006, p. 2):

> [SD] is about safeguarding the Earth's capacity to support life in all its diversity and is based on the principles of democracy, gender equality, solidarity, the rule of law and respect for fundamental rights, including freedom and equal opportunities for all. It aims at the continuous improvement of the quality of life and well-being on Earth for present and future generations. To that end it promotes a dynamic economy with full employment and a high level of education, health protection, social and territorial cohesion and environmental protection in a peaceful and secure world, respecting cultural diversity.

Thus, since the beginning of the 1990s, SD has acted as the meta-narrative in the process of European integration, framing and legitimising the integration project (Baker, 2007, p. 313). The EU stated that it was guided by the Brundtland Report and by the related UNCED process (Baker, 2000). In its original, Brundtland interpretation, SD could be seen as a relatively radical and transformative project. Although the overall tenor of the report was the importance of growth, it insisted on the need to 'change the quality of growth', both by making it less energy and material intensive and more equitable. It also explicitly stated that growth rates needed to be faster in developing than in developed countries (WCED, 1987, p. 49). Most pointedly, the report identified the need for developed countries to 'reduce per capita consumption [of energy] and encourage a shift to non-polluting sources and technologies' (WCED, 1987, p. 59). At the core of the Brundtland variant of SD, therefore, was a challenge to the industrialised world to keep consumption patterns within the bounds of the ecologically possible and set at levels to which all can reasonably aspire (Baker, 2006a).

4 Sustainable consumption: a key element of the European Union's sustainable development strategy

In Section 3, I argued that in their rhetoric, EU institutions demonstrated a strong commitment to the promotion of the Brundtland variant of SD because it was a strategy that fitted with values that provided legitimacy to the project of European integration. In this section, I will interrogate this commitment by taking a closer look at what the European Commission (2004, p. 5) identified as 'one of the key priorities for the EU in the follow-up to the WSSD' – sustainable consumption. In this document (European Commission, 2004, p. 7), the Commission stated that '[s]ustainable consumption and production is at the core of SD'. The EU's policies and practices in relation to SC were developed in parallel with national, Organisation for Economic Cooperation and Development (OECD) and UN initiatives through more than a dozen international conferences from 1994 (more on these in Section 4.2), all seeking to build on the Rio conference.

4.1 The concept of sustainable consumption from an international perspective

The term SC itself can be dated more or less precisely to Agenda 21 – the main policy document to emerge from the 1992 UNCED conference (Jackson, 2006, p. 3). Since then, SC has become a prerequisite for the

Figure 4.4
Selected ethical labels used in the UK. Organic food certification by the Soil Association, the concept of integrated farming (here the LEAF Marque) and the Fairtrade Mark were discussed in Book 2, Chapter 6. The Energy Saving Trust was discussed in Book 1, Chapter 1

The Soil Association organic symbol

The Soil Association is the oldest of the nine, DEFRA-approved organic food certification bodies operating in the UK in 2009. Its organic standards are set by committees made up of Soil Association licensees and industry representatives, cover both the EU organic food regulations and the Compendium of UK Organic Standards and include standards for food and drink, farming and growing, health and beauty, textile, ethical trade, acquaculture industry, livestock markets and woodland. Crops are grown without chemical insecticides and artificial fertilisers. Only limited use of antibiotics is allowed and no growth hormones are allowed in raising poultry and livestock.

The FAIRTRADE Mark

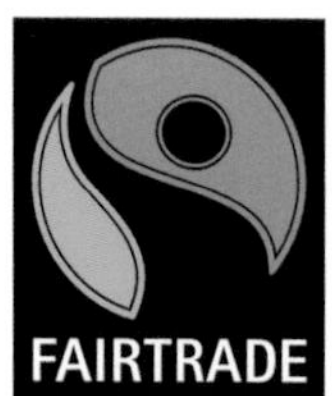

The FAIRTRADE Mark is a registered certification label for products sourced from producers in developing countries. For a product to carry the FAIRTRADE Mark it must meet international Fairtrade standards which are set by the international certification body. Fairtrade labelling started in the Netherlands in the late 1980s. The first products with the FAIRTRADE Mark in the UK became available in 1994. The purpose of Fairtrade labelling is to give farmers and workers in developing countries a better deal than under the conventional trading system through a guaranteed minimum price to cover costs of production and an extra premium for social and economic development.

The LEAF Marque logo

The Linking Environment and Farming (LEAF) organisation was set up in 1991 to encourage farmers to care for the environment by: rotating crops, managing hedgerows to provide habitats and food for wildlife; limiting use of pesticides and fertilisers; recycling waste; conserving energy; minimising pollution; water management; leaving buffer strips between crops and waterways as wildlife corridors; increasing biodiversity by planting trees and keeping wider field margins. LEAF and the concept of Integrated Farming is now a part of a Europe-wide movement European Initiative for Sustainable Development in Agriculture (EISA).

achievement of SD: 'Without sustainable consumption, ... sustainable development is impossible' (Fuchs and Lorek, 2005, p. 261).

Chapter 4 of Agenda 21 called for the adoption of SC patterns. It suggested that consumption patterns in developed countries might not be sustainable: 'In many instances, this SD will require reorientation of existing production and consumption patterns that have developed in industrial societies and are in turn emulated in much of the world' (UNCED, 1992, chapter 4, paragraph 4.15). The proposed solutions included promoting eco-efficiency and using market instruments for

The EU Energy Label

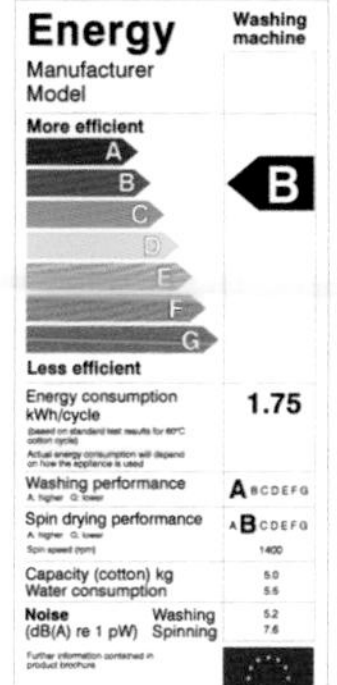

The framework Energy Labelling Directive 92/75/EEC came in to force in 1992 and its first implementing directive on freezers and refrigerators was adopted in 1994, with directives on washing machines, dishwashers, ovens, light bulbs and cars adopted in the following years. The directives promote energy efficiency of these products through compulsory labelling, rating them from A to G, A being the most energy-efficient and G the least. As with all EU directives, energy labelling directives are implemented through EU member states' legislation.

The Energy Saving Trust logo

The Energy Saving Trust is a non-profit advisory organisation in the UK. It awards its Energy Saving Recommended logo to products that meet energy efficiency criteria that are stricter than those required by the EU statutory label. In addition to products covered by the EU Energy Label, the Energy Saving Trust's logo endorses products exempted from the EU Energy Label such as TV sets, boilers and glazing. The criteria are set by an independent panel.

The FSC logo

The Forest Stewardship Council (FSC) is a non-governmental, non-profit international organisation with headquarters in Bonn, Germany and offices in more than 45 countries, including the UK. It was established in the early 1990s. There are three types of FSC certification: forest owners and managers who want to prove that their forest operation is socially beneficial and managed in an environmentally appropriate and economically viable manner can apply for Forest Management Certification. FSC Chain of Custody is for companies that manufacture, process or trade in timber and want to demonstrate to their customers that they use responsibly produced raw materials. The FSC Controlled Wood certificate allows products that mix FSC certified wood with non-FSC wood, but not wood produced in the most socially and environmentally damaging ways.

shifting consumption patterns, but it also called on governments to develop 'new concepts of wealth and prosperity which allow higher standards of living through changed lifestyles and are less dependent on the Earth's finite resources and more in harmony with the Earth's **carrying capacity**' (UNCED, 1992, chapter 4, paragraph 4.11).

In UNCED parlance, **carrying capacity** refers to the maximum size of population that the Earth can support without detrimental effects.

In the early 1990s, SC was a pluralistic concept accommodating two partly complementary and partly competing perspectives. The **reformist model of SC** can be characterised by prioritising different (including ethical but not reduced) consumption that can be achieved either by the reduction in resource consumption per consumption unit due to improvements in production processes or by an environmentally friendly design (Fuchs and Lorek, 2005). These resource efficiency gains are based upon an assumption that individual consumers' choices steered by product labelling (see Figure 4.4), consumer education and environmental taxation drive market transformation towards the provision of greener goods and services. No changes in social and economic structures and lifestyle are required. In contrast, the **alternative model of SC** implies reductions in the levels of consumption in affluent societies in the North. This requires changes in infrastructures and motivations for consumption.

The **reformist model of SC** refers to resource efficiency gains achieved by market transformation driven by consumers' choices. No change of lifestyle is required.

The **alternative model of SC** refers to reduced levels of consumption which implies lifestyle changes.

The problem with the reformist approach is that reductions in resource consumption based on efficiency alone are very often outweighed by a growth in consumption volumes due to increased efficiency (the so-called **rebound effect**) (Greening et al., 2000). There is no guarantee that the growing number of green consumers buying ever-growing numbers of sustainable products produced by increasingly efficient production processes will necessarily result in reduced levels of resource consumption (see Box 4.3 for further discussion on material resource consumption and how it differs from economic consumption). Yet, since the mid 1990s, international and national institutions concerned with SC have increasingly prioritised the reformist perspective and marginalised the alternative perspective. The conceptual shift in which the goals of SC were supposed to be achieved primarily by changes in production processes was reflected in a semantic change which affixed the phrase 'sustainable consumption' to the word 'production' (sustainable consumption and production – SCP).

The **rebound effect** refers to growing demand for goods and services as a result of increased technological efficiency.

Box 4.3 Material resource consumption or economic consumption?

One of the many confusing tensions underlying the debate on SC is the question of what is consumed in the consumer society. There is an important (although not always very clearly articulated) difference between *material resource consumption* and *economic consumption*. Material resource consumption – with its attendant implications for resource scarcity and environmental degradation – has been the principal focus of many of the policy debates on SD. But economic consumers do not only buy and consume material resources. Rather, they consume a variety of goods and services, which employs a variety of different kinds of material inputs and gives rise to a range of different material and environmental impacts. Some forms of resource consumption take place outside of the economic framework. Some forms of economic consumption involve virtually no resource consumption at all.

Source: Jackson, 2006, p. 6

Activity 4.5

How would you explain the prioritisation of the reformist variant of SC in international debates on consumption and the environment? To formulate your answer, you might find it useful to revisit the discussion of liberal environmentalism in Book 2, Chapter 9.

Reformist SC appears to be a manifestation of liberal environmentalism. It is based on the premise that free markets can deal with environmental problems and that economic development is enabling for environmental protection, since more affluent people tend to value the environment more highly. The reliance of reformist SC on market transactions based on consumers' choices corresponds with the emphasis which liberal environmentalism places on the use of market instruments for environmental policy. At the same time, the marginalisation of the alternative perspective of SC is not surprising. The alternative variant of SC defies some of the most fundamental principles on which developed societies are based. Advocating reduced levels of consumption is to 'undermine the key structural role that consumption plays in economic growth' (Jackson, 2006, p. 6). Apart from this fundamental objection, another reason is the difficulty of formulating a policy response with which governments could intervene in this area. Let me now turn your attention to how the EU coped with this challenge.

4.2 Sustainable consumption in the European Union

During the 1970s and 1980s EU environmental policy focused primarily on the regulation of production via emissions limit values and technology standards. This kind of response to environmental problems was limited to technological measures in the sphere of production with minimal, if any, encroachments on people's lifestyles and behaviours. By the end of the 1980s, however, it was becoming apparent that no matter how strictly production was regulated, important environmental problems would remain (Murphy, 2001); the sphere of consumption began to attract the growing attention of policy makers. Although adopted measures did not yet constitute a distinct policy area, the EU began to develop legislation addressing environmental problems from the perspective of consumption. Two early examples of EU measures in the area of consumption were the ecolabelling scheme agreed in 1992 (EEC Council Regulation No 880/92) and the Packaging and Packaging Waste Directive adopted in 1994 (EC Council Directive 94/63/EC).

UNEP as an actor in global environmental politics was introduced in Book 2, Chapter 7 and in this book, Chapter 1

Since then the EU and several of its member states have launched a number of SC initiatives and have taken part in wider international efforts orchestrated by international organisations such as the United Nations Environment Programme (UNEP) and OECD. These activities culminated in the WSSD in 2002. Denmark took an active part in the preparation of WSSD and initiated the development of the 10-year Framework of Programmes on SCP under its council presidency (Fuchs and Lorek, 2005). *The Plan of Implementation*, the most important outcome of the conference, subsequently called on governments to 'encourage and promote the development of a ten-year framework of programmes in support of regional and national initiatives to accelerate the shift towards sustainable consumption and production' (UN/WSSD, 2002, chapter III, clause 14).

The March 2003 European Council identified SCP and the development of the 10 Year Framework Programme as one of the key priorities of the EU in the follow-up to the WSSD and indicated its ambition for international leadership by stating that its goal was 'putting our own house in order by delivering at home what we would like others to do too' (European Commission, 2004). The EU took part in the so-called Marrakech Process, launched at the first Expert Meeting on the 10 Year Framework of Programmes for Sustainable Consumption and Production held in Marrakech in 2003 under the auspices of UNEP and the United Nations Department for Economic and Social Affairs (UN/DESA). This meeting was the first in a series of global and regional expert meetings. *Sustainable Consumption and Production in the European Union* (European Commission, 2004), a document prepared by an expert working group of the Commission, was published in 2004. In the same year, the

European Commission, UNEP, UN/DESA and the Belgian, Finnish, German and Swedish governments organised a meeting on priorities of the EU in the area of SCP and on implementation strategies.

The actions arising from the *Review of the EU Sustainable Development Strategy* (Council of the European Union 2006) included, under the heading 'Sustainable Consumption and Production', tasks for the Commission to propose an EU SCP action plan and to extend performance labelling schemes from electrical appliances and cars to other group of environmentally harmful products. It also called on member states to support information campaigns with retailers to promote sustainable products, including those that stem from organic farming and fair trade. The Council of Ministers also called on the Commission and member states to support green public procurement (Council of the European Union, 2006).

Online Exercise 17

Now log on to the course website and complete Online Exercise 17: *Sustainable consumption in Europe.*

4.3 The transfer of sustainable consumption governance

So far in this section, I have followed the development of SC as a topic of international discussions and strategic directions at the level of the EU and in the wider international context. Using the policy transfer of SC governance to the Czech Republic (Jehlička and Smith, 2008; Smith and Jehlička, 2007) as a case study, I shall now examine the variant of SC governance promoted by the EU and other international actors in the context of a former state-socialist country that was soon to become a new member state of the EU.

Activity 4.6

While reading the following case study think back to the two perspectives on SC introduced in Section 4.1. How would you describe the variant of SC promoted in the Czech Republic by UNEP and the EU? Which of the three modes of Europeanisation introduced in Section 2 would best characterise this process?

SC as a policy concept first arrived in the Czech Republic in 2003, a year before the country's accession to the EU. UNEP ran a series of seminars under the title 'Sustainable Consumption Opportunities for

Europe (SCOPE)' in selected European countries. The UNEP seminar in the Czech Republic was held in May 2003, with participants from the state administration, NGOs, research institutes and business. The main target group was environmental NGOs. The project's aim was to help them improve communication strategies for information on consumption, consumer products and the environment, and to foster training and networking activities.

Two pilot projects were implemented in parallel. Some aspects of the operation of the premises of the Ministry of the Environment in Prague and of the Brno-based Ombudsman's Office were 'ecologised', for example, by switching to recycled copy paper and fitting the buildings with energy saving light bulbs. In the area of food, the internal directive stipulated that only drinks in returnable bottles and catering which used organic food would be used at official functions organised by the ministry (Kašpar, 2004; Vondrouš, 2004).

The greatest challenge proved to be getting several organic meals a day on to the menu in the Ombudsman's Office canteen. Developing the supply network of organic ingredients for the organic lunch option in a country where most of the 800 organic farms specialised in meat production for export turned out to be a difficult task. Subsequently, the organic meal option was also introduced in a Brno kindergarten. Nevertheless, despite these huge logistical efforts, after about six months both schemes were scrapped due to low demand for the organic meal option, mainly because of its substantially higher price (Kanichová, 2004). Apart from green procurement, most other initiatives in the area of SC took the form of the dissemination of information for consumers including campaigns promoting ecolabels and setting up a web-based calculator of ecological footprints.

UNEP's one-off initiative in the Czech Republic was soon transformed into an EU-sponsored initiative for a ten-year framework of programmes on SCP, identified by the March 2003 European Council as one of the EU's key priorities. In anticipation of the country's EU membership, the Czech government set out to develop the *10 Year Action Plan for Sustainable Consumption and Production*. To that end, a working group on SCP was set up as one of several such groups within the Czech government's Council for Sustainable Development (Kašpar, 2004).

In interviews which Joe Smith and I conducted with leading figures of the Czech SC initiative, both from within government and among NGOs, the respondents appeared sceptical about reduced levels of consumption as a basis for policy. Instead, when voicing their ideas on policy proposals for SC, they invoked the neoliberal vocabulary, including the market, choice, the citizen-consumer and the individual responsibility of citizens for the consequences of their consumption:

> And then, I think that a group of people is emerging [in the Czech Republic] to whom status is not simply a new house, but a house built according to ecological principles. And these are the people who are well enough off to afford it, and they are different from the category of people with the alternative lifestyle, who really leave [the city] for the countryside and seek to be self-sufficient and live independently from the external world.
>
> (Kanichová, 2004)

They placed the range of policy solutions to consumption-related environmental problems firmly in the area of voluntary and primarily informative instruments:

> When somebody says sustainable consumption, to me that means responsible consumption and that is informed consumption. In short, when I make a decision as a consumer, I make that decision on the basis of information.
>
> (Kašpar, 2004)

At this point you should attempt to formulate your answers to the two questions in Activity 4.6. To me, the case study shows that SC promoted by both the EU and UNEP was of the reformist variant, which relies on eco-efficiency and market transformation through consumers' choices. As you have seen, policy instruments chosen to promote SC were economic, such as green public procurement, and informative, such as ecolabelling, organic food labelling, certification schemes, consumer advice and information, consumer campaigns and education. The opinions of the Czech SC policy community, who were dismissive of reduced levels of consumption, were in keeping with the views of the former head of the UNEP Division of Technology, Industry and Economics (UNEP/DTIE) (the division of UNEP in which its SC programme was housed) who stated that 'sustainable consumption was not about consuming less, it was about consuming differently, consuming efficiently, and having an improved quality of life' (UNEP/CDG, 2000 cited in Fuchs and Lorek, 2005).

As to the question about the mode of Europeanisation, the policy transfer in the case study seems to be a combination of the latter two 'softer' means of influence: first, shaping domestic political opportunity structures by offering national actors new points of leverage to achieve domestic change and, second, affecting national beliefs and perceptions indirectly through the publication and dissemination of strategic documents.

One of the most intriguing aspects of the arrival of SC in the country was that it generated no interest in the rich set of existing and well-established consumption practices that were compliant with the principles of SD. One area particularly illustrative of this contrast was food consumption. The two specific examples of sustainable food consumption promoted by the SC initiative – fair trade and certified organic food – were marginal phenomena. For example, in 2006, Czech citizens spent an equivalent of £125,000 on fair trade products (Kovařík, 2007) and only 0.06 per cent of food sold in the country in 2003 was organically produced (Pokorný, 2004). This contrasted with widespread SC practices such as food self-provisioning, barter and gifting, and forest product harvesting.

The exact environmental benefits of food self-provisioning are difficult to establish, given the variety of practices. Nevertheless, it seems that, beyond the virtues of self-fulfilment and authenticity that food self-provisioning affords, there are a number of environmental benefits associated with this practice. These include a shorter distance from the garden to the table than for food acquired in a conventional way in shops and often a virtually organic standard of cultivation. In addition, as we also found out, through barter and gifting, food self-provisioning fosters social solidarity and networking.

The traditional self-provisioning on allotments or smallholdings outside the cities expanded significantly during the state socialist period. However, it did not disappear with the arrival of Western consumerism in the 1990s. The national survey of 1100 respondents that we commissioned in 2005 showed that this style of provisioning was still widely practised: 41.5 per cent of the population used a garden or allotment to produce vegetables and fruit for their own consumption (Jehlička and Smith, 2008). The evidence from the survey as well as from household interviews confirmed Adrian Smith's (2002) earlier findings from Slovakia that these practices did not develop simply as a result of hardship. Both during state socialism and the post-socialist period, the non-economic reasons for these practices have been at least as prominent as the economic ones. The Czech evidence suggested that there were higher rates of self-provisioning in more financially secure households. The proportion of people with high living standards that grew their own food was higher (43.6 per cent) than the proportion of people doing so with the lowest living standard (35 per cent). Thirty-five per cent of entrepreneurs had a production garden.

Twenty-one per cent of Prague dwellers grew fruit and vegetables; in mid-size towns this proportion was 41 per cent and in villages with less than 2000 inhabitants, 65 per cent. The main stated reason for food self-provisioning was access to healthy food. The second motive was financial and the third was that it was a hobby. Our household interviews confirmed that there was still a lot of barter going on:

> I have plenty of eggs and rabbits and it is quite unhealthy to eat too much of these. As I have a lot of friends, I give a couple of eggs or a rabbit or exchange them for, say, lettuce and other vegetables or for leftovers which I then feed the rabbits.
>
> (Ryklová, 2005)

Barter and gifting of fruit and vegetables among both family and friends networks was practised in large cities as much as in rural areas. In addition, a number of urban and rural dwellers alike picked a range of wild berries and mushrooms that they consequently used in their kitchens. Clearly, self-provisioning, allotments and forest products harvesting helped to sustain dense webs of connection between the rural and urban in ways that were comparatively rare in Western Europe.

Figure 4.5
Allotments in northern Bohemia, Czech Republic

Online Exercise 18

Now log on to the course website and complete Online Exercise 18: *Researching food self-provisioning in the UK*. This is an opportunity for you to learn more about food self-provisioning as an alternative and sustainability-compliant social practice.

Figure 4.6
Czech farmer and simplifier Daniel Maláč in his farmhouse kitchen

Our interviews revealed that food self-provisioning did not register with the Czech SC policy network as an SC practice, since they were dismissive of 'alternative lifestyles' and 'self-sufficiency', and branded these practices as ineffectual. At the same time, the protagonists of the network were aware of another social phenomenon related to SC. The Kanichová quotation on page 163 referred to voluntary simplicity – a phenomenon frequently debated in the Czech media.

Voluntary simplicity is a choice out of free will to limit expenditure on consumer goods and services and to cultivate non-materialistic sources of satisfaction and meaning.

Voluntary simplicity denotes the choice out of free will – rather than by being coerced by poverty – to limit expenditure on consumer goods and services, and to cultivate non-materialistic sources of satisfaction and meaning (Etzioni, 1998). While warning about the undue conflation of the values and motives of environmentalists (concerns for nature and the ill effects of the growing use of scarce resources) and simplifiers (i.e. adherents of voluntary simplicity, whose psychological needs require other pursuits than conspicuous consumption), Amitai Etzioni is nevertheless unequivocal about voluntary simplicity's environmental benefits: 'There can be little doubt that voluntary simplicity, if constituted on a large scale, would significantly enhance society's ability to protect the environment' (Etzioni, 1998, p. 638).

In comparison with the socially universal appeal of food self-provisioning, voluntary simplicity was a relatively marginal phenomenon in the Czech context and its adherents had a specific social profile. The Czech sociology professor Hana Librová, who conducted long-term research into the phenomenon (Librová, 1994, 2003), described them as 'people who resist the general idea of a society oriented towards attaining high levels of consumption'. Most of them were people who 'moved from comfortable conditions in towns to live in the country'. The furnishing of their flats was markedly modest, even poor. The respondents did not have a car or a TV set by choice. The great majority of them had a secondary or university education, which, however, was not used professionally (Librová, 1994, p. 208). These people were not ecological activists, but they were involved in attempts at awakening and renewing life in local communities. They typically owned a large garden where they grew organic vegetables and fruit. Many of them were vegetarians. To a significant extent, their food consumption relied on self-provisioning. One feature that characterised these households was the possession of bicycles, whose number usually corresponded to the number of family members. Librová (1994, p. 210) concluded that ecological benefits were not a primary reason for their modest lifestyle. Instead, these emerged as a side effect of their engagement in non-consumptive activities. In Etzioni's terms, Czech voluntary simplifiers adopted consumption practices that led to considerably reduced material resource consumption (see Box 4.3).

The Czech case study also illustrates the lack of interest of actors such as the EU and UNEP in local approaches to SC, in particular those that contradict the neoliberal underpinnings of the reformist variant of SC. Neither the external policy exporters nor the domestic recipient community made any attempt in their interaction to consider the possibility of domestic sustainable practices. The case study demonstrates how from the early 1990s the scope of the discussion on SC in the EU and international organisations, including UNEP and the OECD, narrowed from a wider perspective that allowed consideration of the redefinition of prosperity and the transformation of lifestyles and focused instead on politically acceptable and economically rational approaches. In this it is illustrative of *course theme 2*.

Ecological modernisation was introduced in Book 1, Chapter 6. There is a close affinity between liberal environmentalism (introduced in Book 2, Chapter 9) and ecological modernisation. The latter is primarily used in the European context

Box 4.4 shows that the EU adopted and promoted the reformist variant of SC – in other words 'more consumption of more efficiently produced products by better informed consumers' – which shared its key features with ecological modernisation as formulated by Bruno Milanez and Ton Bührs (2007). These key features included: the idea of institutional restructuring of the industrial system manifested in the emphasis placed on resource efficiency, innovation and diffusion of new technologies; flexible and participatory environmental policy instruments such as voluntary agreements, **eco-management and audit schemes (EMAS)** and green taxes; the idea that growing environmental awareness leads to an increase of green consumption, which in turn motivates producers to develop cleaner products and services to gain competitive advantage; and the idea of decoupling environmental impact and economic growth.

Eco-management and audit schemes (EMAS) is an EU voluntary programme in which organisations that meet certain environmental performance criteria become EMAS registered.

Box 4.4 The European Union's understanding of sustainable consumption and production

In 2004 the European Commission published an inventory of policies, activities and instruments relevant to SCP under the title *Sustainable Consumption and Production in the European Union*. The document claimed that it provided 'a factual "photograph" of what was being done at the EU level'. The inventory stated that:

- Decoupling environmental impacts associated with the use of natural resources from economic growth was an important strategy for the achievement of SCP.
- SCP required an integrated approach to policy making and that the nine configurations of the Council of Ministers in charge of EPI needed to step up their efforts.
- Development and dissemination of environmental technologies were critical factors for SCP.
- Integrated product policy was a means of reducing the environmental impacts of consumption and was a way of creating the right framework for a market that favours environmentally friendlier products.
- Providing consumers with relevant information and thus helping them to make appropriate choices as well as awareness raising on corporate social responsibility (CSR) were both instrumental for SCP. One tool to guide consumers to choose products of high environmental quality was the EU ecolabel.
- Market instruments, such as taxes or tradable permits, were instruments for support of SCP.

Source: European Commission, 2004

Activity 4.7

What are the benefits and problems of the reformist approach to SC?

The approach has the benefit of being more achievable in contemporary consumer democracies, and is at least a limited step forward. It clearly encourages individuals to think about social and environmental consequences of their behaviour and to consider the difference they can make through their consumer choices, rather than leaving environmental policy to politicians.

However, it ignores the wrong price signals that the market sends due to the environmental and social externalities. The focus on the actions of individuals reduces environmental implications to considerations of personal choice and fails to recognise the socially situated and socially structured character of consumption. For that reason, the reformist perspective on SC fails to recognise the power asymmetry between an individual atomistic consumer and organised and globalised corporate interests which the consumer is supposed to influence in an effort to resolve environmental problems. As Michael Maniates (2002, p. 45) pointed out, 'when responsibility for environmental problems is individualised, there is little room to ponder institutions, the nature and exercise of political power, or ways of collectively changing the distribution of power and influence in society'.

The concept of externality was introduced in Book 1, Chapter 3

Despite the limited potential of the reformist variant of SC to alter consumption patterns, it would be imprudent to dismiss it entirely. In contrast to the policy perspective, the two variants of SC can be considered as complementary from the perspective of everyday life. I suspect that this is how many people who seek to modify their consumption behaviour would perceive them. Clearly, in many instances, the everyday practices of the same individual fall in both categories of SC. It may well be that reformist SC is a stepping stone on the way to a more profound variant of SC (Seyfang, 2005).

5 Conclusion

Drawing on the discussions in the chapter I'd like to turn the Conclusion into an evaluative exercise.

Activity 4.8

To what extent, in your view, does EU environmental governance constitute a model for others to follow?

You've learnt in this chapter how, despite the absence of legal provision for environmental competence in the founding treaty, the EU not only developed an internal environmental policy, but also became a global environmental leader. Since the early 1990s the EU has embraced the concept of SD. To the EU, SD, with its emphasis on inclusiveness, equality, justice, social cohesion, well-being and environmental protection was an attractive concept that offered the expanding and increasingly heterogeneous EU a means of fostering a sense of shared values and legitimacy and enabled it to develop a discernible identity vis-à-vis the external world. SD provided an opportunity for mobilising popular support for the project of European integration.

The EU has not only developed its model of environmental governance and sought to implement it internally, as you have seen in the discussion of the process of Europeanisation, but it has also promoted this model beyond its borders. The adoption of environmental *acquis communautaire* was a condition of the former state-socialist countries' accession to the EU in 2004 and 2007. Furthermore, as you've also seen, the adoption of EU environmental norms was part of action plans the Union concluded with countries participating in the European Neighbourhood Policy. The Commission sought to integrate principles of SD in all new trade agreements. The EU is increasingly making its external relations informed by, and conditional upon, a catalogue of norms (Baker, 2006a, p. 78). According to some scholars, the norms have become so central to the European project that they refer to the EU as a 'normative power' (Manners, 2002). In this sense, the emphasis which the EU places on SD as a norm is a continuation of the more idealistic motives for European integration.

Historically, EU enlargements and the need to adopt environmental *acquis* were perceived by accession countries as an improvement and innovation in their domestic environmental policies. As you have seen in Section 4.3, this also applied to the countries that joined the Union during the two mid 2000s enlargements. Both government officials and environmental NGOs considered the adoption of environmental *acquis* as a significant innovation of domestic policy. The Czech case study showed that even given their own pre-existing set of domestic sustainability-compliant practices, the domestic policy community regarded the EU SC governance as a major innovation.

The EU's variant of SC, increasingly conceptualised by the EU as a key prerequisite for the promotion of SD, has been referred to as an example to the wider world. However, the tension between the need for identity formation and pursuit of legitimacy for the EU on the one hand and the commitment to the growth and competitiveness of European business on the other was manifested in the prioritisation of the reformist over the alternative variant of SC.

In practice, in contrast to the rhetoric, the EU's approach to SC adhered to principles of ecological modernisation and favoured fostering economic competitiveness and growth, thus eschewing the Brundtland Report's imperative about the need for the industrialised world to keep consumption patterns within the bounds of the ecologically possible and at levels to which all can reasonably aspire. To sum up, the EU's SCP practices are a positive step towards SD, but they fall well short of the aspirations that the EU has itself articulated. More needs to be done if the EU, and the world, are to live up to the challenges set by the Brundtland Report.

The EU has itself admitted that the exclusive reliance on the reformist variant of SC might be problematic:

> ....[t]echnological development and innovation have increased resource efficiency and enabled environmental gains. These gains are, however, often outweighed by increased consumption and changes in lifestyle, such as increasing mobility. There are also growing disparities in consumption levels between developed and developing countries as well as a widening gap between the wealthy and the poor.
>
> (European Commission, 2004, p. 5)

Nonetheless, as Rechtshaffen's introductory article reminds us, despite this critique, the EU's model of environmental management is often seen with envy by the outside world. And as Baker (2006a) argues, however disenchanting the practical application of the principles of SD in the EU might be, what is important is that the EU has launched Europe on a path towards SD and enshrined this commitment in the treaties.

Video 7

Now watch Video 7: *Low carbon housing.*

Audio 8

Now listen to Audio 8: *Environmental politics at a time of crisis.*

References

Avery, G. (2008) 'The EU and wider world' in Bomberg, Peterson, and Stubb, (eds) (2008), pp. 179–200.

Baker, S. (2000) 'The European Union: integration, competitions, growth and sustainability' in Lafferty, W. M. and Meadowcroft, J. (eds) *Implementing Sustainable Development: Strategies and Initiative in High Consumption Societies*, Oxford, Oxford University Press, pp. 303–37.

Baker, S. (2006a) *Sustainable Development*, London and New York, Routledge.

Baker, S. (2006b) 'Environmental values and climate change policy' in Lucarelli, S. and Manners, I. (eds) *Values and Principles on European Union Foreign Policy*, London and New York, Routledge, pp. 77–96.

Baker, S. (2007) 'Sustainable development as symbolic commitment: declaratory politics and the seductive appeal of ecological modernisation in the European Union', *Environmental Politics*, vol. 16, no. 2, pp. 297–317.

Baker, S. and McCormick, J. (2004) 'Sustainable development: comparative understandings and responses' in Vig, N. J. and Faure, M. C. (eds) *Green Giants? Environmental Policy of the United States and the European Union*, Cambridge, MA, MIT Press, pp. 277–302.

Baker, S. and Welsh, I. (2000) 'Differentiating Western influences on transition societies in Eastern Europe: a preliminary exploration', *Journal of European Area Studies*, vol. 8, no. 1, pp. 79–103.

Bomberg, E., Peterson, J. and Stubb, A. (eds) *The European Union: How Does it Work?* (2nd edn), Oxford, Oxford University Press.

Bomberg, E. and Stubb, A. (2008) 'The EU's institutions' in Bomberg, Peterson, and Stubb, (eds) (2008), pp. 45–70.

Caddy, J. (1997) 'Harmonisation and asymmetry: environmental policy co-ordination between the European Union and Central Europe', *Journal of European Public Policy*, vol. 4, no. 3, pp. 318–36.

Council of the European Union (2006) *Review of the EU Sustainable Development Strategy (EU SDS) – Renewed Strategy*, Brussels, Council of the European Union; also available online at http://www.oecd.org/dataoecd/41/9/38834376.pdf?contentId=38834377 (Accessed 24 May 2008).

Dinan, D. (2008) 'How did we get there?' in Bomberg, Peterson, and Stubb, (eds) (2008), pp. 22–44.

Etzioni, A. (1998) 'Voluntary simplicity: characterization, select psychological implications, and societal consequences', *Journal of Economic Psychology*, vol. 19, no. 5, pp. 619–43.

European Commission (2004) *Sustainable Consumption and Production in the European Union*, Luxembourg, Office for Official Publications of the European Communities.

Fuchs, D. A. and Lorek, S. (2005) 'Sustainable consumption governance: a history of promises and failures', *Journal of Consumer Policy*, vol. 28, no. 3, pp. 261–88.

Greening, L. A., Green, D. L. and Difiglio, C. (2000) 'Energy efficiency and consumption – the rebound effect – a survey', *Energy Policy*, vol. 28, pp. 389–401.

Haas, P. (1964) *Beyond the Nation-state: Functionalism and International Organization*', Stanford, CA, Stanford University Press.

Hildebrand, P. (2005) 'The European Community's environmental policy, 1957 to "1992": from incidental measures to an international regime?' in Jordan, (ed.) (2005), pp. 19–41.

Jackson, T. (2006) 'Readings in sustainable consumption' in Jackson, T. (ed.) *The Earthscan Reader in Sustainable Consumption*, London, Earthscan, pp. 1–23.

Jehlička, P. and Smith, J. (2008) *An Unsustainable State: Contrasting Food Practices and State Policies in the Czech Republic*, paper presented at the European University Institute Alumni Conference, Florence, Italy, 20–21 June.

Jehlička, P. and Tickle, A. (2004) 'The environmental implications of Eastern enlargement of the European Union: the end of progressive EU environmental policy?', *Environmental Politics*, vol. 13, no. 1, pp. 77–95.

Jordan, A. (ed.) (2005) *Environmental Policy in the European Union*, London, Earthscan.

Jordan, A. and Liefferink, D. (2004a) 'The Europeanisation of national environmental policy' in Jordan, and Liefferink (eds) (2004b), pp. 1–14.

Jordan, A. and Liefferink, D. (eds) (2004b) *Environmental Policy in Europe: The Europeanisation of National Environmental Policy*, London, Routledge.

Kanichová, K. (2004) Interview, Nadace Via, Ostrava, 16 August.

Kašpar, J. (2004) Interview, Ministry of the Environment, Prague, 31 May.

Knill, C. (2001) *The Europeanisation of National Administrations: Patterns of Institutional Change and Persistence*, Cambridge and New York, Cambridge University Press.

Kovařík, P. (2007) 'Férová cesta do Rakouska', *Sedmá Generace*, vol. XVI, no. 4, pp. 24–6.

Librová, H. (1994) *Pestří a Zelení: Kapitoly o Dobrovolné Skromnosti*, Brno, Veronica and Hnutí Duha.

Librová, H. (2003) *Vlažní a Váhaví: Kapitoly o Ekologickém Luxusu*, Brno, Doplněk.

Maniates M. (2002) 'Individualization: plant a tree, buy a bike, save the world?' in Princen, T., Maniates, M. and Konca, K. (eds) *Confronting Consumption*, London, MIT Press, pp. 43–66.

Manners, I. (2002) 'Normative power Europe: a contradiction in terms?, *Journal of Common Market Studies*, vol. 40, pp. 235–58.

Manners, I. (2006) 'The constitutive nature of values, images and principles on the European Union' in Lucarelli, S. and Manners, I. (eds) *Values and Principles in European Union Foreign Policy*, London and New York, Routledge, pp. 19–41.

Milanez, B. and Bührs, T. (2007) 'Marrying strands of ecological modernisations: a proposed framework', *Environmental Politics*, vol. 16, no. 4, pp. 565–83.

Murphy, J. (2001) 'From production to consumption: environmental policy in the European Union' in Cohen, M. J. and Murphy, J. (eds) *Exploring Sustainable Consumption: Environmental Policy and the Social Sciences*, Oxford, Pergamon, pp. 39–58.

Pokorný, M. (2004) 'Biosedláci v zemi bůčku', *Respekt*, vol. XV, no. 32.

Rechtschaffen, C. (2006) 'Will the environmentalists find their voice?', *San Francisco Chronicle*, 4 January, p. B-9 [online], http://sfgate.com/cgi-bin/article.cgi?f=/c/a/2006/01/04/EDGV9GFGJG1.DTL (Accessed 24 May 2008).

Ryklová, I. (2005) Interview, Stěžery, 29 March.

Sbragia, A. M. (2005) 'Institution-building from below and above: the European Community in global environmental politics' in Jordan (ed.) (2005), pp. 201–24.

Sbragia, A. M. and Damro, C. (1999) 'The changing role of the European Union in international environmental politics: institution building and the politics of climate change', *Environment and Planning C: Government and Policy*, vol. 17, no. 1, pp. 53–68.

Seyfang, G. (2005) 'Shopping for sustainability: can sustainable consumption promote ecological citizenship?', *Environmental Politics*, vol. 14, no. 2, pp. 290–306.

Smith, A. (2002) 'Economic practices and household economies in Slovakia: rethinking "survival" in austerity' in Smith, A., Rainnie, A. and Swain, A. (eds) *Work, Employment and Transition: Restructuring Livelihoods in Eastern Europe*, London, Routledge, pp. 227–45.

Smith, J. and Jehlička, P. (2007) 'Stories around food, politics and change in Poland and the Czech Republic', *Transactions of the Institute of British Geographers*, vol. 32, no. 3, pp. 395–410.

United Nations Conference on Environment and Development (UNCED) (1992) *Agenda 21: The United Nations Program of Action from Rio* [online], http://www.un.org/esa/sustdev/documents/agenda21/english/agenda21chapter4.htm (Accessed 24 May 2008).

United Nations/World Summit on Sustainable Development (UN/WSSD) (2002) *Plan of Implementation* [online], http://www.environment.gov.za/Documents/Documents/Summit_ImplementationPlan/wssd_pi_12-22.htm (Accessed 24 May 2008).

Vogel, D. (2005) 'The hare and the tortoise revisited: the new politics of consumer and environmental regulation in Europe' in Jordan (ed.) (2005), pp. 225–51.

Vogler, J. (2005) 'The European contribution to global environmental governance', *International Affairs*, vol. 81, no. 4, pp. 835–50.

Vondrouš, D. (2004) Interview, Ministry of the Environment, Prague, 31 May.

Weale, A., Pridham, G., Cini, M., Konstadakopulos, D., Porter, M. and Flynn, B. (2000) *Environmental Governance in Europe: An Ever Closer Ecological Union?*, Oxford, Oxford University Press.

World Commission on Environment and Development (WCED) (1987) *Our Common Future*, Oxford, Oxford University Press.

Zito, A. (2005) 'The European Union as an environmental leader in a global environment', *Globalizations*, vol. 2, no. 3, pp. 363–75.

Chapter 5
Look out: ethics and citizenship

Mark J. Smith

Contents

1 Introduction

Reflecting on the first four chapters of Book 3, it seems that their message is only marginally more positive than that of earlier parts of the course. Some encouraging examples of environmentalist practice and some promising ideas give grounds for hope, but overall they remain secondary to economic imperatives. Even the European Union (EU), arguably the second most powerful political and economic entity in the world, practices less than it preaches in terms of sustainable development (SD) because of strong economic interests and pressures. So the problem faced by this last chapter is similar to that addressed by Book 3 as a whole: some promising responses to environmental problems are happening, but even the most promising are still 'too little and too late', so the problems are getting worse.

This chapter responds to this problem by turning its back on the focus on what is actually happening in the generation of environmental problems, actual political responses and the factors that frustrate environmental policy. Instead, it focuses on 'what should be done?'

The chapter addresses this question in three stages. First, it does this by looking back at some of the many value judgements explicit or implicit in earlier parts of the course, where certain things were identified as desirable and others as undesirable. Second, it seeks to clarify some of the moral principles used to make those value judgements and considers how philosophical ethics attempts to justify or criticise particular moral positions. Third, it notes that, in a liberal society, individual citizens are expected to choose, argue for and live by their own moral standards, subject only to respecting other people's rights to do the same.

1.1 Learning outcomes

This chapter should enable you to:

- recognise some of the main values embedded in earlier parts of the course
- understand some basic ideas and approaches from philosophical ethics that can help environmentalists make sense of ethical issues
- recognise our individual responsibility, as citizens, to contribute to environmental governance.

2 Look back: ethics and values in DU311

The purpose of this section is to refresh your memory of the major discussions of values in earlier parts of the course, hence to lay a foundation for the further development of ideas about values in the following two sections. Each book is considered through a brief summary and an activity.

Book 1 starts by showing that contending values inhibit responses to global warming as much as does scientific uncertainty. Chapter 1, Section 3.2 describes attempts to use the principle of 'common but differentiated responsibility' to relate different levels of responsibility to different countries, but the chapter also points to a variety of value positions, from ecocentrism, through the precautionary principle, intragenerational equity to SD and the doctrine of 'contraction and convergence'. Chapter 2 goes on to show that in the debates over climate change science has been shown to be influenced by values, while the 'deniers' seemingly see the growth of the economy as more important than any environmental problem, perhaps influenced by neoliberalism. Chapters 3, 5 and 6 have more detailed discussions of a number of value positions, which are addressed in Activity 5.1.

Activity 5.1

Compare and contrast the principles underpinning neoliberalism (Book 1, Chapter 3) and human security (Book 1, Chapter 5).

Does the discussion of ethics in Chapter 6 help to resolve the clash of value positions?

Interestingly, both neoliberalism and human security derive from liberal values, though they have taken different lines within that tradition. Graham Dawson explains in Chapter 3 that the core liberal principle is to protect individuals and allow them to live their lives as far as possible as they please, so the role of the state is to protect diversity and maintain law, property and security. He explains that neoliberalism links to an extreme version of liberalism, called libertarianism, which demands that individuals be given as much liberty as possible, regardless of other outcomes, including any concern with equality. Human security, however, as explained by Amartya Sen in Chapter 5, suggests that secure living requires social and economic provision, by the state if necessary, so that all individuals have real opportunities to participate in society. This seems consistent with Graham Dawson's encapsulation of liberalism as demanding that all individuals should have as much liberty as any other, and is sometimes described as 'freedom to' in contrast with libertarian 'freedom from'.

Andrew Blowers's discussion in Chapter 6 criticises ecological modernisation as a normative guide and advocates a stronger version of SD in which ecocentric values, justice and equity play stronger roles. In so doing he is more consistent with the goal of human security than with neoliberalism. However, he also compounds the ethical problem: his discussion of intergenerational equity connects back to Graham Dawson's discussion of discounting in model building and economic calculation and the problem of finding an appropriate balance between present and future generations – an issue which is difficult for liberal theory because we can't be at all sure what future generations will want for themselves.

Andrew Blowers's discussion suggests that a stronger version of SD may be preferable to environmentalists and is broadly consistent with Claudia Aradau's case for human security as a criterion. However, it does not resolve the tension between these positions and neoliberalism. This is because libertarians are as unlikely to accept government intervention to promote sustainability or equity as are the national governments that regard national security as the overriding justification and the national interest as more important than international agreement on a policy capable of halting climate change.

Overall, Book 1 certainly shows that a variety of value positions and ethical principles is in contention in international environmental politics, but leaves a lot to be done to clarify the nature of the contention, let alone to resolve it in principle or practice.

In its handling of values, Book 2 poses a more complex problem than does Book 1: it deals with a wider variety of issues and values, and often in a less explicit way. This results from the task given to authors – to discuss particular issues in relation to the first three course questions but not the fourth. It follows that values are referred to explicitly only when they are part of the way particular problems are caused, responded to, or those responses frustrated. However, they are ever present in the ways problems are defined and in the emphasis on different explanatory factors – indeed, the different ways of framing problems are emphasised from the first chapter of the book. As you have probably noticed in your role as a critical reader, most course team members tend to be more or less disenchanted with contemporary international policy, most believing it to be excessively influenced by neoliberalism, but with a range of interpretations and explicit or implicit value preferences.

I'll try to make these explicit in the next few paragraphs, but of course this will be my interpretation, and you should read it critically, check against the text of the chapters and reflect on your interpretation and preferences.

The first three chapters of Book 2 address the causes of environmental problems and open up the question of how society has interpreted them and responded to them. My reading of these chapters is that they point to the industrialisation of society since about 1750 as a key process, allowing population to grow rapidly and living standards to be transformed, though with massive inequality. Each chapter adds detail and value questions. Chapter 1 argues against seeing population growth as a major problem, and hence is critical of state policies to reduce population growth, pointing both to women's rights and religious values as policy makers' reasons for not attempting to influence population. Chapter 2 points to industrialisation as a double-edged sword, creating environmental degradation as well as increased consumption, queries the tendency to equate economic growth with 'development' and points to a variety of political arrangements that have shaped the form and effects of industrialisation, from free-market capitalism to state socialism via the mixed economy. Chapter 3 identifies urbanisation as both cause and consequence of industrialisation and inequality, and points to a need for greater democracy in urban governance if environmental problems are to be tackled. Taken together, the three chapters combine to argue that environments, and the distribution of benefits and harms, are socially constructed, both materially and in discourse, and can potentially be shaped by changing the form of governance, locally and globally.

Chapters 4–6 follow this up, examining the way that environmental problems link society and nature, the local and the global, and pose questions of governance and policy. They also begin to ask a new value question. Chapter 4 shows water to be 'uncooperative' and queries how far we are entitled to treat it merely as a resource, before raising further questions about how that resource should be allocated. The intrinsic value of nature is even more in question in Chapter 5, in the form of species and ecosystems, even before its re-definition as biodiversity to be conserved. Implicitly, and then explicitly, these two chapters reopen the question of ecocentric values: does nature, physical and/or biological, have as much right to exist as do humans, or are we entitled to alter them for our own use? Almost all the interpretations and values from the book so far surface in Chapter 6, so it is worth spending some time on the following activity.

Activity 5.2

Look again at Book 2, Chapter 6 and answer the following two questions:

How does it reflect the interpretations and values sketched in the paragraphs above?

Can you see one way in which it identifies a new way of asserting values?

The chapter reflects the wider interpretations of the book when it argues that the productivity and problems of contemporary agriculture stem from it having been industrialised. This is not just a question of technology: agriculture is said to be inherently political, also geographical and profoundly unequal. Mainstream food networks reflect economic and political power structures; indeed, they help separate reality from ideology, since they do not reflect free-market ideals, but exhibit high concentration of ownership of the means of distribution and retain many barriers to international trade. One of the alternatives the chapter addresses, organic farming, responds at least in part to the concerns of ecocentrics, since it is intended to be more consistent with conserving biodiversity. The other alternative, fair trade, is more socially innovative, since it relies on affluent consumers prioritising ethical values over price, facilitated by new processes of certification. It points to the 'politics of consumption' as an alternative to political participation for some citizens.

Chapters 7–10 add further instances and depth to discussions of the range of values raised in earlier parts of the book, but end with a new perspective. Chapter 7 deals centrally with the realities of international negotiations, stressing the role of perceived national interests, including the concerns of states with sovereignty, economic growth and competitiveness, and concluding that agreements are stronger and better implemented when there is a shared benefit at low cost, as with ozone. The Convention on International Trade in Endangered Species (CITES) does reflect some ecocentric concerns, and hazardous wastes highlight international inequality, so the motives for agreement are more altruistic, but the agreements consequently weaker. International environmental law is extensive, and does state some clear principles, including the precautionary principle, but is currently more diffuse and less powerful than trade law, though emerging ideas in 'green criminology' might change that. Chapter 9 renews the earlier critique of neoliberalism, showing not only how it emphasises profit and hence encourages exploitation of the environment and workers, but also how it subverted the concept and practice of SD and led to increased inequality. Chapter 10 takes a less hostile view of neoliberalism and proposes a new ethical principle derived from it.

Activity 5.3

Review Book 2, Chapter 10, identify its ethical proposal and consider whether it seems likely to change the status quo.

The ethical proposal is clear: the idea that corporate social responsibility (CSR) might contribute to achieving environmental and social goals more effectively than would state intervention. You need to make your own mind up about its potential effectiveness, but my suspicion is that, however responsibly some corporations may want to behave the realities of economic competition against unscrupulous 'bottom feeders' will ensure that they will fail.

Overall, Book 2 identifies a range of values whose neglect exacerbates social and environmental problems, but it has not been set the task of translating those values into future policy. That task is addressed by Book 3, the content of which is so fresh in your memory that we can move straight to an activity.

Activity 5.4

Revise the first four chapters of Book 3 and consider the following two questions:

1 What resolution of the tension between economic and environmental policy emerges similarly in the proposals made in Chapter 1 and the actual developments discussed in Chapter 4?

2 What social and environmental values are given new prominence in Chapters 2 and 3?

In relation to international governance, Chapter 1 proposes that linking a World Environment Organisation (WEO) that would consolidate international environmental policies to a World Trade Organization (WTO) that would take seriously the issue of fair competition in international trade could force attention to inequality, labour and environmental standards, and hence both coordinate and enforce trade and environmental policies. Chapter 4 describes how the EU found it necessary to agree regional, health, environmental and labour standards to transform the idea of a single market into fair competition internally, though pressures from economic interests and competition from abroad reduced the ambition for SD into the practice of the weaker ecological modernisation, albeit supplemented by the idea of sustainable consumption (SC).

Chapter 2 points to environmental justice as a compelling demand, able to mobilise disadvantaged groups to act in relation to environmental problems, revive the environmental movement and influence some governments to change policy. Chapter 3 recognises that, explicitly or implicitly, environmental justice is also the claim of disadvantaged groups within the South and of the South in relation to the North. Chapter 3 also points towards the need to consider ecological resilience as part of environmentalism and to change the principles of accounting and economic calculation to recognise the economy as dependent on environment and society rather than as the ultimate goal of human existence.

Up to this point in the course, therefore, a tension has been established between the real world, dominated by the discourse of neoliberalism, resting on libertarian values, a range of social critiques on the basis of values like intra- and intergenerational equity or human security, and ecocentric claims, for biodiversity and resilience. In succession to an integration of social and environmental claims through Brundtland's concept of SD, there now seems to be a more plausible case for environmental justice, or its near synonym, 'just sustainability'. Yet, however persuasive the call for environmental justice might be, in practice it remains pitted against the vested interests embodied in international power politics and business competition. Although these are usually presented as pragmatic or realistic, they rest on conservative values, in that they resist change, accept existing hierarchies, both of military and political power and of property and wealth, and argue that national security justifies strengthening state authority and curtailing individual liberties.

How can we, as students and citizens, set about evaluating and reconciling these claims?

3 Ethics: the systematic study of moral questions

In most traditional human societies, individuals would have been in little doubt about what actions were seen as right or wrong, good or evil, since these were clearly expressed in a moral code, often derived from religion, and hence backed by divine authority. Today, individuals are confronted with many new moral questions, including those concerning the environment, but greater mobility and easier communications have made people aware of many different moral positions and cast doubt over any particular moral code. How then can we make sense of the moral choices we face in everyday life and in making policy? In this section, we are going to look at some ideas from **philosophical ethics** – the systematic study of moral questions.

Philosophical ethics is the systematic study of moral questions.

I am aware that this is the last chapter of the course and that no one wants to meet a lot of new abstract ideas at this stage. However, I have already shown that the course has opened up many questions about values and ethical issues, so I have designed this chapter to try to answer, or at least clarify, the questions that have arisen, and offer you some help in revising the course and preparing for the exam. Because ethical principles were formulated in particular historical and cultural contexts, I start with some attempts to argue for ways of defining the good society, before moving on again to ask how those approaches link to environmental values.

3.1 Normative ethics: how can we decide what's good or right?

An initial point is that, unless we are willing to remit this question to an authoritarian state and abide by its decision, in asking this question we are adopting a liberal or anarchist position, for they are the doctrines that insist on individuals' entitlements to make choices for themselves. Liberalism accepts that an appropriately limited state can provide the context in which individuals can exercise choice, but anarchists reject the state altogether. In a world where states are well established, I'm going to assume that some form of liberalism is the realistic choice available to citizens. However, liberalism in the philosophical sense spans a range from right- to left-wing politics in everyday terms, provided there is some role for individual liberty.

Moral philosophers have debated rational bases for ethics over centuries without any particular approach being able to persuade everybody or refute the others. Three main approaches remain in contention, stressing rights and obligations, consequences, and virtue respectively.

3.2 Rights and obligations: deontological approaches

One broad approach to ethics is to try to establish the rights and obligations of individuals, and is named after the Greek words for the study of duty (*deon* meaning duty and *logos* meaning science). This stretches back at least to the Stoics, who pointed out that even slaves had freedom of thought. There are three main approaches to this process, two of which involve a comparison between a 'state of nature' and society.

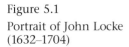

The **natural rights tradition** is based on the notion that there are natural laws and rights that exist in nature and across different societies.

The first approach – the **natural rights tradition** – is based on the notion that there are natural laws and rights that exist in nature and across different societies, even if not recognised by local laws. Bear in mind that these ideas originated 400 years ago as secular ideas began to challenge theological interpretations of the role of humanity. They sought to define the meaning of human nature and what sort of social and political arrangement (the relations between citizens and between the state and citizens) was appropriate based on their definition of the natural propensities of the human species. The right to life is widely accepted, but further extensions, even to liberty, are contentious. Nonetheless, this tradition is seen as significant in its effects on the English common law, and is still appealed to by critics of the state.

A particularly influential formulation of natural rights was that of John Locke (1988 [1690]) (Figure 5.1), who argued for rights to property, established by working on land or materials taken from nature, as well as to liberty. His views influenced both the Glorious and American Revolutions and remain influential today. He saw property rights as derived initially by working the land and as transmitted through fair contract. As well as being part of a natural rights approach, Locke can also be seen as part of a second approach.

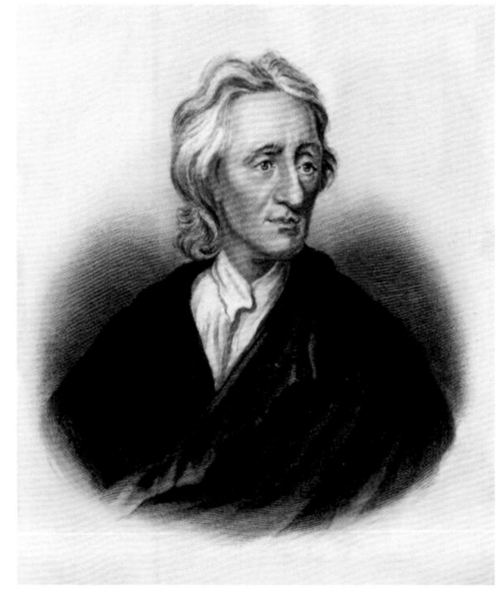

Figure 5.1
Portrait of John Locke (1632–1704)

Contractarian approaches argue through the notional agreement between individuals and the state, in which individuals surrender some natural rights for benefits provided by the state.

The second approach to the identification of rights and duties is through the idea of a 'social contract', a notional agreement between individuals and the state, in which individuals surrendered some natural rights for benefits provided by the state. **Contractarian approaches** were constructed against a reference point of some natural (or pre-social) state of affairs. If we pose a state of nature made up of human beings who are predatory, aggressive and purely self-interested then the social contract is inevitably a means of constraining this war of each against all through voluntary submission to a sovereign who would enforce order (Hobbes, 1991 [1651]). If you pose natural people as cooperative and fundamentally well meaning (a noble savage) then the contract is designed to enhance these capacities through popular sovereignty (Rousseau, 1997 [1762]).

A more influential account of the state of nature was presented by Locke, who characterised natural 'man' as acquisitive and possessive. In this account, the appropriate social contract is a mechanism allowing individuals to transform nature into property while at the same time accepting some restraints on their freedom as a necessary sacrifice to protect their own private property. This acts as the foundational principle behind the 'rule of law', interpreted by impartial judges to reconcile disputes and address grievances in liberal political systems. Fundamental to this approach is the view that the rule of law is preferable to rule by 'men' because it should eliminate the arbitrary exercise of power by rulers. In short the assumptions about the fundamental character of humanity became the baseline for thinking about what a social contract ruling moral and political behaviour should be. Curiously, since the 'state of nature' was a key input to this approach, it has subsequently been applied largely to social issues, with little regard to the rights of any part of nature other than humans.

A third approach to the establishments of rights and obligations has been the tradition established by Immanuel Kant (Figure 5.2) in the 1780s. Unlike the contracts considered above, it replaces speculation about some putative human nature with an emphasis on rationality. Kant identified what he called the 'categorical imperative' – in other words the universal requirement. This was that we should 'act only according to that maxim whereby you can at the same time will that it should become a universal law' (Kant, 2005 [1785]). The meaning of this abstract requirement becomes more apparent when linked to the second requirement – to treat human beings as ends in themselves and not as means to an end. In effect, the **categorical imperative** highlights that what applies to one should apply to all and requires all people in all circumstances to 'do as they would be done by' and hence promotes a fair society.

The **categorical imperative** highlights that what applies to one should apply to all and requires all people in all circumstances to 'do as they would be done by' and hence promotes a fair society.

To sum up, it is worth noting that although each approach produces plausible arguments for certain rights and obligations, none is conclusive. The right to life is widely agreed, as is the need to balance one's own rights against those of others. However, even liberty, the central liberal claim, is compromised by the role of the state in preserving order and law. The right to property is subject to honest acquisition and transfer. Other rights are even more dependent on

Figure 5.2
Portrait of Immanuel Kant (1724–1804)

the community and the state. Although Kant's logic is more difficult to follow, his approach is perhaps the clearest in promoting fairness and justice.

3.3 Consequentialism

An alternative approach to those seeking to establish rights is to focus on the consequences of actions rather than the actions themselves. This approach was pioneered by utilitarians. For Jeremy Bentham (1996 [1789]) (Figure 5.3), the most rational way of making a judgement was to identify the pain and pleasure (or, if you prefer, suffering and enjoyment) which followed as a consequence of a decision. If the pleasure exceeded the pain then the action was worthwhile (and, logically, if pain exceeded pleasure then it was not). The aim of Bentham's project was to maximise the sum total of human well-being. He described the process through which we weigh up the costs and benefits involved as the 'felicific calculus'. This approach avoids any problems of defining individual rights or virtues, but has three problems of its own. **Consequentialism** applies moral judgements only to outcomes and not to intentions or behaviour, so it does not matter if individual behaviour is selfish, self-deceiving or dishonest if its consequences for the aggregate is good. It requires a definition of well-being and a way of calculating the balance of pleasure and pain, posing a formidable practical challenge. It admits the possibility that a good outcome for the many would justify harm to a minority. Although 'the greatest good for the greatest number' seems an appealing idea, it proved difficult to operationalise.

Consequentialism is an approach to ethics that focuses on the desirability of the consequences of behaviour, rather than on the desirability of intentions or motivations.

Figure 5.3
Portraits of Jeremy Bentham (1748–1832) (left) and John Stuart Mill (1806–1873) (right)

Later developments of this approach both attempted to identify principles at an individual level that would promote the general good, and also addressed the idea that there are clear differences between human capacities to experience pain and pleasure. John Stuart Mill (1977 [1859]) (Figure 5.3) developed utilitarian assumptions to propose a meritocratic system of governance whereby those with higher faculties have greater voting strengths than those with lower faculties.

Activity 5.5

How does the environmental justice movement (EJM), discussed in Chapter 2, combine deontological and consequentialist approaches?

The movement challenged the situation where certain ethnic groups suffered a disproportionate concentration of pollution. This is the consequence of residential segregation and choice of industrial sites. This unequal outcome breached the legal rights of minorities. Having started with a grievance about the distribution of pollution, the movement went on to claim rights to recognition by, and participation in, decision-making processes.

The deontological and consequentialist traditions, both of which seek to establish ethical principles which apply universally, have dominated the discussion of environmental ethics for the last fifty years but a third strand has re-emerged alongside them, which does not place such a strong emphasis on universal ethics but puts a stronger emphasis on how citizens understand right conduct – the tradition of virtue ethics.

3.4 Virtue ethics

The identification of virtues that promote responsible practices is not a new development and virtue ethics as a tradition draws on ancient Greek (particularly through the writings of Aristotle), Chinese and Buddhist philosophy (on the latter two, see Pangsapa and Smith, 2009). The account of virtues considered here focuses on character formation rather than being concerned with contractual rules or calculations as to consequences. It depends on individuals taking responsibility for their own actions and often going beyond or against what is expected or required under the conventions and laws of their society. Relevant virtues include practical wisdom (prudence), temperance, courage, justice, faith, hope, compassion, self-sacrifice, kindness, honesty, benevolence, mercy, forgiveness and friendship. The return to virtues in ethical and political discussions offers some interesting new ways of thinking about the meaning of obligation, where the cultivation of the character of the self acts as a route to the regard of others. However, there is concern that we should take care not to privilege one kind of virtue such as compassion or justice as the basis of all other virtues.

As Rosalind Hursthouse (1998) argues, adopting virtue ethics does not mean that we should not have rules and principles, merely that as we decide what is virtuous or a vice we will devise rules such as 'act honestly' or 'don't be cruel'. These do not specify what is right and wrong or what is good or bad in an absolute way. What is generous or mean depends on context – or as Hursthouse (1998, p. 69) describes, 'is socially or culturally determined' – but this does not mean that virtue ethics dispenses with the right or good. Indeed, virtuous citizens may act according to one of these in some circumstances, but also may draw upon other virtues in other situations. In addition, virtues are defined as being found between deficiency and excess. For example, courage as a virtue is distinct from its deficiency (cowardice or timidity) and its excess (foolhardiness or recklessness). In the case of all virtues the ideal place is in the 'golden mean'. Precisely what the mean means is not defined in advance, so this allows for flexibility in addressing the mix of issues in a specific situation.

Activity 5.6

Review Section 3 so far and sum up what you see as the main conclusions for ethical individual behaviour.

How does that summary relate to libertarianism, social critique and ecocentrism?

My own conclusions are as follows: No single approach has refuted the others, so ethical behaviour needs to balance rights, consequences and virtue. The right to life is broadly agreed, as is the need to accord the same rights to others as one claims for oneself, but further rights depend on speculative assumptions about the state of nature and/or the social contract and are open to dispute. The categorical imperative obliges everyone to refrain from exploiting others and claiming privileges which cannot be shared by all. Consequences may be difficult for individuals to predict, but once consequences are apparent, we should adjust our behaviour. Living virtuously means behaving better than we have to.

Libertarianism, based on the claim that individuals should have as much liberty as possible, with the state guaranteeing property, contract and security, and with no regard to fairness of outcome or virtue of the individual, is an extreme position, reliant solely on a rights claim that most positions regard as questionable and failing other ethical tests. Social liberalism or democratic socialism, with their focus on positive freedom, seem more consistent with a range of ethical approaches, unless the state were to tax, legislate and regulate so extensively as to violate the ability of individuals to live as they choose. Ecocentrism is not provided for in these approaches, since they deal only with ethical principles for humans.

3.5 Normative ethics and the environment

As the environment emerged as an issue, some scholars began to ask what ethical principles might apply to the relationship between society and environment. Some of these remained focused on the principles that would benefit humans, and SD is an example of an 'anthropocentric' principle. Others sought to take the interests of nature more seriously, and are described as 'ecocentric'. Much of this work sought to extend existing approaches to normative ethics to apply to part or all of nature. A key strategy was to extend the 'moral community' beyond existing humans and ask whether some parts of nature should be treated as morally considerable. The idea of **moral considerability** involves addressing the question of whose interests should be taken into consideration within the terms of a particular moral approach. In the past it has even been restricted to a minority of humans (the nobility, higher social classes, males and particular ethnic groups). In addition, these restrictions have been couched in terms of humans who are able to engage in rational thought and this has been applied at different times to exclude slaves, women, ethnic minorities (or in the case of South Africa, ethnic majorities) and people with disabilities. Animal welfare campaigners and environmental ethicists have attempted to extend moral considerability to individual animals, non-human species and broader conceptions of the environment from the land, trees, river systems, mountain ranges, oceans and bioregions to the global ecosystem or biosphere (Nash, 1989).

Moral considerability involves addressing the question of whose interests should be taken into consideration within the terms of a particular moral approach.

To illustrate the logic, it is useful to focus on non-human animals. Peter Singer (1976) argues that we should consider higher animals as worthy of consideration in the same way as we give rights to children or people supposedly unable to exercise 'rational faculties'. In short, Singer suggests that we need to consider the existence of different capacities for pain and pleasure in human and non-human animals. Singer suggests that we should recognise some of the higher animals as 'sentient', and that their capacity to feel pain should be included in utilitarian calculation. Utilitarian accounts argue that any act should be motivated by a conscious calculation to maximise the greatest good for the greatest number. In short, the sum total of pleasure that follows from the act should exceed the total pain and suffering. For instance, it could be argued that the pleasure experienced by many human beings from an extension of life which follows from scientific experimentation for medical purposes may outweigh the suffering experienced by animals in the vivisection laboratory. This is an extreme case and many calculations would be more finely balanced and complicated by trying to take account of the potential harm to the different categories in Figure 5.4. If we take account of the capacity for sentiency of higher order animals, according to Singer this would lead to a transformation in animal welfare by ending:

- intensive animal farming
- systematic tests used in cosmetics and medical experiments when alternatives are available (including tests such as LD50 – a standard toxicity measure – whereby a substance is administered until 50 per cent of the animals involved have reached a 'lethal dose')
- hunting and trapping for furs (other than for survival)
- the use of animals in entertainment
- maltreatment of domestic pets.

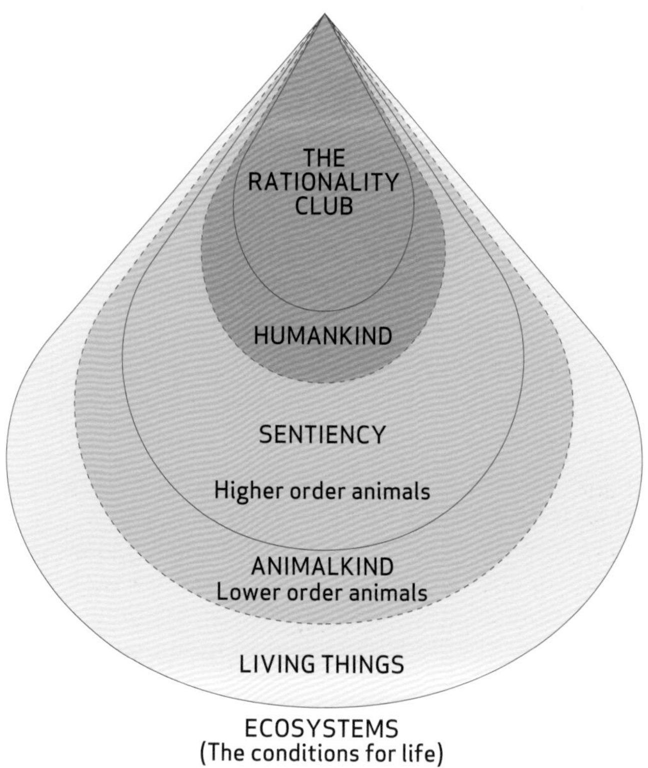

Figure 5.4
The ethical teardrop: who and what is morally considerable? (Source: Smith and Pangsapa, 2008)

As a result (and as indicated in Figure 5.4) a moral community can be defined in different ways, from including only part of the human species, the existent human species (possibly including future generations) or even go beyond it to include higher order animals such as primates and dolphins and broader conceptions of the natural world. Some environmental activists who advocate deep ecology go even further and ask us to imagine what kind of world we would have if we started from the assumption of biocentric equality where all aspects of the ecosystem have rights that human animals must respect. Deep ecologists Bill Devall and George Sessions (2000 [1985]) develop the arguments of Arne Naess to argue:

> all things in the biosphere have an equal right to live and blossom and to reach their own individual forms of unfolding and self-realization within the larger Self-realization. This basic intuition is that all organisms and entities in the ecosphere, as parts of the interrelated whole, are equal in intrinsic worth. Naess suggests that biocentric equality as an intuition is true in principle, although in the process of living all species use each other as food, shelter, etc. Mutual predation is a biological fact of life and many of the world religions have struggled with the spiritual implications of this. Some animal liberationists who attempted to side-step this problem by advocating vegetarianism are forced to say that the entire plant kingdom including rain forests have no right to their own existence. This evasion flies in the face of the basic intuition of equality.
>
> (Devall and Sessions, 2000 [1985], p. 195)

For these environmental writers, beyond satisfying our vital needs, we do not have any rights to reduce nature's richness and diversity – one of the basic principles of deep ecology. For some, this must be quite frightening in its implications – should I cut the grass in my lawn, can I swat a fly, can I crush an insect, slug or a snail when I walk, should I drown a spider in the bath or the toilet and should I poison a rodent or ant infestation on my property without infringing their right to live and blossom?

While some religions adopt extremely scrupulous positions over the killing of any animal and many individuals choose to be vegetarians or vegans, most societies admit the rights of nature only through animal welfare legislation and the practice of nature conservation, most recently in the form of biodiversity policies, as discussed in Book 2, Chapter 5. Even from an anthropocentric point of view, taking ethics seriously can benefit nature in at least three ways, two resting on the idea of human flourishing and the third on intergenerational ethics.

First, since liberalism rests on the basic principle that people should be free to live the life that they want to, subject only to the rights of others, if people choose lifestyles that rely on contact with a flourishing nature – for example, as birdwatchers, walkers or eco tourists – they will tend to sustain nature.

Second, if we recognise that the lives of many humans depend on the environment (as argued in Chapter 3) and we behave ethically towards those people – for example, in not supporting practices that immiserate them – we will tend to sustain those environments.

Third, if we take into account the welfare of future generations, who might want more contact with nature than we do, we need to keep that option open for them by not allowing species to go extinct and conserving resources and a full range of natural ecosystems. The common expectation that future generations will be better off than we are, combined with the argument about the Environmental Kuznets Curve, makes it very plausible that future generations will be more environmentalist than we are.

The Environmental Kuznets Curve was introduced in Book 2, Chapter 2.

David Schlosberg (2007) analyses the concept of environmental justice, as practised in the USA and global movements and as debated by ethical theory. He argues for a concept of justice that combines environmental justice – addressing the distribution of environmental benefits and harms, the recognition and participation of all groups in decision making, and ensuring that all groups have the capability of living their version of the good life – with ecological justice – justice to nature itself. He notes that there is a variety of theoretical interpretations of these issues and welcomes this pluralism. He insists that society should reflect on its interactions with nature and make arrangements to represent natural interests in political processes through deliberative democracy. Only through debate, implementation and social learning will environmental justice be achievable.

In conclusion, environmental responsibility and a greater respect for nature can be promoted in various ways but what is right, good and virtuous often depends on the specific environmental issue and the cultural and political context in which environmental problems are constructed. This chapter has been engaged in highlighting the range of ethical approaches that is encountered in social and environmental discussions and all have been relevant in one way or another.
As a result, for practical reasons, this chapter acknowledges moral pluralism. In the absence of any single standard of behaviour, individuals need to balance rights, obligations, consequences and virtues in deciding how to live.

Activity 5.7

Reflect on your lifestyle in the light of the ethical criteria discussed above:

1 Might your behaviour have consequences for the rights, pleasures or pains of others?

2 Can your behaviour be universalised?

3 How far are you prepared to extend moral considerability to poor people in the South, to animals or to future generations?

4 Are you virtuous?

4 Citizenship and the environment

This section explores the role that citizens might play in protecting the environment. It starts with a brief introduction to the concept of citizenship, focuses on proposals from one major author in the field and introduces a brief case study that discusses the transformative potential of ethically motivated citizenly behaviour. This is followed with some critiques of those proposals and concludes by suggesting some options for citizen identities.

4.1 Citizenship: a brief introduction

Citizenship is concerned with individuals' relationships with the public domain – their status and activities vis-à-vis the state. The concept first arose in the city states of ancient Greece, where citizens were those who shared in the political process, both taking part in deliberations and in decision making. Citizenship was typically limited to adult male property owners, with women, children, slaves and foreigners excluded. According to one major tradition of thought on citizenship – now referred to as **republican citizenship** – to be a citizen is to be a member of a political community, with certain responsibilities and duties (Seyfang, 2006). This tradition demands that citizens prioritise the interests of their political community over their personal interests.

Republican citizenship is concerned with responsibilities and duties that citizens have to act in the interest of the common good.

A different concept of citizenship was pioneered in the Roman Empire and has become the norm in the liberal democratic nation states which have developed since the seventeenth century. This concept, now defined as 'liberal citizenship', includes all nationals of a state, and in some cases all residents of a territory, who are protected by the law, have some influence over government through voting and lobbying, but exercise their freedoms mainly in the private sphere. **Liberal citizenship** places emphasis on the rights of individuals within the framework of the rule of law. The rights and duties of liberal citizens may vary between countries and over time, and in most democratic countries there has been a movement from recognition of substantial welfare rights in the 1960s and 1970s towards more minimal welfare in the neoliberal era.

Liberal citizenship places emphasis on the rights of individuals within the framework of the rule of law.

The meaning of citizenship has been influenced by globalisation. Movement of people has made most countries' populations more diverse, eroding the sense of community and mutual responsibility, and creating problems in defining appropriate rights for minorities. Fears of international competition have made many governments less responsive to ordinary citizens and more concerned with business interests, often contributing to a sense of alienation and apathy among voters. The internationalisation of the economy has created connections between workers in distant countries and consumers in the developed countries, with new ethical dilemmas about wages and working conditions and the terms of trade. International and global environmental problems have created new responsibilities between gainers and sufferers and new transnational organisations. Both governments and citizens face new challenges, especially when the dominant ideology, neoliberalism, demands that all agents take responsibility for their actions. In this new context, the concept and reality of citizenship are much debated. One recent summary (Leydet, 2008) notes that the status of citizenship was demanded rather than offered and that nothing prevents liberal citizens from engaging in the political process, nationally or internationally, to seek to alter the theory and practice of citizenship.

4.2 Ecological citizenship

Andrew Dobson, in *Citizenship and the Environment* (2003), argues that 'ecological citizenship' goes beyond both the liberal and republican concepts of citizenship. It focuses on both duties and rights. Ecological citizenship has to be international because the issues are international. He calls his approach 'post-cosmopolitan', because it goes beyond cosmopolitanism, which, as discussed by Andrew Linklater (1998), focuses on open and more intense dialogue. This, plus the institutional conditions for creating bonding, develop a sense of belonging to the broader human community, so we recognise the needs of strangers out of compassion (as a 'good Samaritan'). However, charity has its limits, for it can be withdrawn or even maintain the dependence of the recipient. Others focus on the issues of distribution to suggest that environmental harm necessitates the same framework for an open and uncoerced dialogue, but also demands more justice in response to these harms (Caney, 2001).

Dobson argues that globalisation is asymmetrical, with benefits to the powerful and harms to the less powerful. As a result he proposes a new post-cosmopolitan approach that recognises that citizens across the world should be treated as equals and that citizens of developed countries have political obligations to treat others justly. His concept of distributive justice is based on the idea that entitlement to an equal share is established prior to inhabiting cultural identities, that is, it is binding. This means that the latter involves 'a specifically political type of obligation as opposed to a more broadly moral type' (Dobson, 2003, p. 29).

Ecological citizenship is a concept of citizenship that is non-territorial and is concerned with the responsibility people have for the implications of their actions on the environment.

Dobson's concept of post-cosmopolitan **ecological citizenship** has four major characteristics. First, it is not territorially bound, but goes beyond existing states. Second, it spans both public and private, influencing personal, economic and political behaviour. Third, it uses the criterion of just distribution of ecological space, requiring over-users of ecological space to reduce their demands in order for under-users to consume more. Fourth, it goes beyond contractual responsibilities to recognise the possibility of unreciprocated and unilateral obligations for citizens. In other words, A owes B as a result of a prior action, undertaking, agreement or relationship that is binding on the actors involved.

Dobson highlights the debate on climate change as prompting consideration of 'bindings' of this kind between Western citizens and other peoples of the world that have been affected by the current and past activities of industries and citizens in developed societies. While this is useful for taking account of past practices, it can be less effective in persuading citizens, companies and governments within industrial societies that their activities are responsible for environmental impacts elsewhere. It took the UK government and energy companies a decade to accept responsibility for the acid rain effects of sulphur dioxide (SO_2) emissions in Western Europe. The refusal of the US government to ratify the Kyoto Protocol, for example, demonstrates how states continue to deny their responsibility for transboundary effects on climate change in order to protect their immediate interests. Resistance to applying greenhouse gas restrictions by countries such as the USA is also couched in terms of making the relationship more reciprocal with rapidly industrialising countries such as India and China.

Dobson also places a special emphasis on the feminist ethics of care as a route to develop a greater sense of responsibility. He argues that the 'citizenly ties that bind' are present in both private and public spheres. Indeed, the language of obligation is increasingly present in discussions of parental responsibilities, antisocial behaviour and personal lifestyle decisions. On the environment, also, responsibility for waste and litter, choosing less resource consumptive means of transportation, energy conservation measures, voluntary conservation activities or local biodiversity monitoring all involve personal or private decisions to reduce the impact of our ecological footprints. So, Dobson makes a distinction between environmental citizenship (the extension of liberal rights such as civil, political and social rights to include access to environmental goods or to prevent environmental bads) and ecological citizenship that seeks to ensure that our ecological footprints do not 'compromise or foreclose the ability of others in present and future generations to pursue options important to them' (Dobson, 2003, p. 120). For Dobson, the first virtue of ecological citizenship is justice and all virtues should contribute to the eradication of environmental injustice. For Dobson, the provision of 'aid' in response to natural hazards should be seen not as benevolent acts of charity but compensatory justice, for the harm inflicted by industrial societies on others is a result of

Ecological footprint, in connection to Andrew Dobson's ideas on citizens' rights, was introduced in Book 1, Chapter 1 human-induced climate change. He argues this alters the nature and source of obligation, for matters of compassion are increasingly seen as citizen relations.

Gill Seyfang set out to research a local organic food network in East Anglia, UK to test her hypothesis 'that ecological citizenship could be an innovative new force to motivate sustainable consumption, and that such motivation might be expressed through purchasing food from local organic food networks' (Seyfang, 2006, p. 393). The main findings from her research are summarised in Box 5.1.

Activity 5.8

While reading the case study in Box 5.1 think back to the discussion on the reformist and alternative models of consumption in the previous chapter. In your view, which of these two models does Eostre Organics promote?

Box 5.1 Eostre Organics and ecological citizenship

Eostre's origins lie within Farmer's Link, a Norfolk-based non-governmental organisation (NGO) which was inspired by the Rio Earth Summit in 1992 with the goal of improving the sustainability of farming in developed countries. Farmer's Link established East Anglia Food Link (EAFL) to promote conversion to organic production in the region. EAFL was inspired by European organic producers' cooperatives and persuaded East Anglian organic growers who were already trading informally to adopt a formal cooperative structure. Eostre was launched in 2003 with a DEFRA Rural Enterprise Scheme grant, with nine local members and one overseas member – the Italian organic producer cooperative El Tamiso, which itself comprised over 50 businesses. Its specific aims included: to supply consumers of all incomes with high-quality seasonal produce; to encourage cooperative working among its members and between the co-op and consumers; transparency about food supply chains; to source all produce from UK and European regions from socially responsible producers and co-ops promoting direct local marketing, and from fair trade producers outside Europe; to minimise packaging, waste and food transport. The cooperative structure and the resulting greater scale and stability of their operation enabled Eostre members to start supplying local markets such as market stalls and box schemes. The co-op supplied produce to thirteen box schemes, fifteen market stalls, nine cafés, pubs or restaurants and twelve shops.

Interviews with Eostre organisers and staff and two surveys of their customers revealed that values and principles expressed by both creators and users of this organic food network were strongly resonant with ecological citizenship. Apart from the motivation related to personal health and safety, they showed a clear commitment to social justice and fairness in trading relationships, to reducing ecological footprints, to cutting consumption levels and sought to make links of solidarity between producer and consumer. Many consumers perceived their everyday consumption decisions as being deeply political and enjoyed the expression of values as a result of this activity. Eostre's consumers demonstrated their ecological citizenship and their moral commitment to SC, rather than simply as a response to market incentives, by explaining their willingness to pay higher prices for locally produced organic food as support of environmentally friendly and socially considerate enterprise. As one respondent commented: '[I like] the sense of communal participation, starting from feeling that we all know – or potentially know – each other, and continuing on through to wider issues, both social and environmental'.

Seyfang concluded that Eostre and its consumers behaved as 'good ecological citizens'. She found Dobson's model of ecological citizenship a useful analytical tool to understanding their values and motivations. Ecological citizenship allows us to conceptualise as citizenly activities that take place in the private sphere such as participation in a local organic food network and that in the two traditional models are not necessarily associated with citizenship. The Eostre case showed that ecological citizenship both motivates private consumption choices and nurtures a need for collective action to build new socio-economic models, thus overcoming the traditional division between individual and collective action.

Source: Seyfang, 2006, pp. 388–94

I'd argue that the local organic food network centred on Eostre co-op was an operation compliant with the alternative model of consumption introduced in the previous chapter. Rather than relying exclusively on 'a citizenship of the market, [in which] purchases are the only votes that count' (Seyfang, 2005, p. 296) or, in other words, on individual consumers' choices exercised within the existing economic structure (that is, the reformist model of SC), the economic model of Eostre depended on the moral commitments and commitments to justice of its customers, on their desire to reduce consumption levels and on their ambition to innovate and alter social infrastructure. The alternative model of SC goes beyond seeing economic behaviour as individuals' responses to price and information and instead conceptualises 'economic behaviour as being intimately embedded within social relations, bringing complex issues to bear on efforts to change behaviour' (Seyfang, 2006, p. 391).

So, as you have seen, ecological citizenship can play an important role in the development of innovative responses to environmental and social problems. Responsible and morally committed citizens can make a difference. However, Seyfang's (2006) research also raises a host of questions to which we do not have answers yet. For example, we need to know more about the conditions under which ecological citizenship emerges and develops, how we account for ecological citizenly and un-ecological citizenly preferences inevitably experienced by individuals and, perhaps most importantly, what are the processes by which private actions translate into collective activities.

4.3 Criticisms of Dobson's concept of ecological citizenship

You will recall the critique of the promotion of organic farming and food as an SD strategy in Book 2, Chapter 6 by Michael K. Goodman and in the previous chapter in this book by Petr Jehlička. However, the concept of ecological citizenship itself has not escaped criticism either. For example, Derek Bell (2003, 2005), a liberal environmentalist, suggests that Dobson's account is both too limited in its objectives and carries a serious danger. It is too limited in at least two respects: if we limit ecological citizenship to those acts that involve sacrificing part of one's own ecological footprint and redistributing space to others with less than their fair share, then many other environmental activities that do not involve redistributing ecological space are excluded. These would include local conservation volunteering and participation in Local Action 21 (formerly Local Agenda 21) consultations. Second, Bell argues that limiting duty to when an actor is personally complicit could let us off the hook if environmental injustice occurs in other societies, committed by other states, or between citizens with whom we have no contact.

Bell (2003, 2005) identifies dangers from a liberal viewpoint. States lack the power to enforce laws to secure for everyone the right to a fair share of ecological space. If persuaded to adopt laws by pressure from a minority, the laws might need forcing through without general consent and could involve imposing restrictions that are inconsistent with liberal values, such as compulsory population control. Hence, Bell is concerned with the potential for eco-authoritarianism, that individual freedoms will be lost because of state intrusion in personal life to achieve environmental goals.

In response to Bell, it is arguable that there are dangers in focusing on individual citizens, for this could privatise the responsibilities of the state. In addition, this focus ignores the need for partnerships between state and civil organisations as well as citizens. Even if one disagrees with Dobson's specific proposals, they highlight a key issue – how do citizens find a way of linking their own understanding of environmental issues with responsible acts that contribute to the collective good? This is where virtue ethics are especially useful for, as indicated above, they link personal development to broader positive impacts. However, is one virtue such as justice enough? Perhaps a more flexible framework that recognises the co-dependence of, and overlaps between, virtues would be more helpful. Being compassionate depends on having courage, while being just often depends on temperance – restraining materialistic appetites, as implied by ecological footprint analysis. When we consider relevant virtues, then the issues become clearer. Practical wisdom (or prudence) is often seen as more compatible with the precautionary principle and notions of environmental stewardship. Potential also exists in using the virtues of temperance, kindness, generosity, humility, simplicity, gentleness, tolerance, forgiveness, self-sacrifice and even stoicism (being resigned to one's fate). The key point is that notions of virtue are not simply imposed; they are cultivated as deliberate attempts to live up to regard for others. Fulfilling obligations thus becomes an honourable act of self-regard, completing one's side of an agreement, living up to a mission, feeling good about one's reputation, being a 'good human being' or leading a flourishing life. There will be dilemmas when adjudicating upon the relative importance of one species compared to another (including the human species) but then, ethical dilemmas are not absent from other approaches and we should not anticipate their absence here either (Barry, 1999, pp. 32–4; Connelly, 2006; Smith and Pangsapa, 2009, pp. 330–5).

The status of citizen opens up the possibilities of taking action in one's private life, in local and national politics and in transnational organisations. Dobson has elaborated arguments for a particular version of ecological citizenship, aimed at a just distribution of ecological space, but the discussion of ethical principles in Section 3 shows that there could be other ways of defining your own objectives as an ecological citizen.

Activity 5.9

If republican citizenship implies a republic, and liberal citizenship a liberal state, what kind of state is implied by ecological citizenship?

At a minimum it needs to be liberal to allow citizens to pursue their own definition of the good life. Ideally, it would also embody ecological virtues: in being internationalist and future oriented, in being just and responsible, in being willing to go beyond collaboration to recognise the need for redistribution to compensate for past exploitation of nature and people. Compared to existing states, there is a long way to go.

5 Conclusion

If we now look back to the value positions identified in Section 2 as underlying many debates in the course, and relate them to principles and proposals in Sections 3 and 4, some tentative conclusions seem possible.

The ethical case for libertarianism as a justification of negative liberty over the state, for unlimited acquisition of private property and cut-throat competition in a free market seems weak, since it is justified only by singling out one approach to identifying rights and setting aside consequences, the categorical imperative and virtue. The stress on property seems to ignore requirements for honest acquisition and fair exchange spelt out by Locke, let alone the more direct critiques of social liberals and socialists. Finally, it is perverse that an approach which rests on assumptions about 'the state of nature' and natural rights has nothing to say about the rights of, or obligations to, nature.

The case for social liberalism or democratic socialism, which underlie appeals to fairness, equity and justice, is consistent with principles dealing with obligations to others, consequences, the categorical imperative and virtue ethics. However, it is far from clear-cut, since liberals differ over whether fairness is defined through equality, merit, need or other principles.

Once we attempt to extend the ethical community to include more than existing humans, problems become quite serious. Most people agree that cruelty to higher animals is wrong, though many become less convinced if it can be shown that it will yield vital benefits for humans, but further extensions of moral considerability to lower animals, vegetables, rocks or ecosystems provoke increasing scepticism. Similarly, many people are eager to include the interests of their children and grandchildren in policy decisions, but the further we go into the future the greater uncertainty about what kind of society and technology they will live in or what they themselves will want. In practice, though, there are plenty of good reasons for treating nature with respect, limiting pollution and conserving species, resources and ecosystems for the benefit of present-day humans, many of whom are the next generations of the families of decision makers. Indeed, the challenge of taking intragenerational equity seriously seems formidable, even without admitting the interests of future centuries.

None of the suggestions above are definitive, and they would probably enrage libertarians and deep ecologists. If society is to be influenced by ethical principles, there need to be debates between citizens to identify what principles command widespread support, and the willingness of people to live with the likely consequences. The cause of environmentalism has been undermined so far by the willingness of a broad public to sympathise with environmentalist objectives, but to insist in practice on a high level of consumption and on voting for politicians who promise more economic growth. If values like equity, justice and sustainability are to have more influence in future, citizens will need to be better informed and clearer about the policies, behaviours and lifestyles that could translate the principles into practice. Perhaps what is needed is a new social and ecological contract that identifies rights and obligations, and desired outcomes, but leaves room for people to exercise virtue. Such a contract could only come about if large numbers of citizens are willing to engage in a transition of society and lifestyle and pressure politicians to take appropriate action. Students of environmental policy are well equipped to take a lead in such a process.

Video 8

Now watch Video 8: *Transition town*.

References

Barry, J. (1999) *Rethinking Green Politics*, London, Sage.

Bell, D. (2003) 'Environmental citizenship and the political', paper presented to the ESRC Seminar Series on Citizenship and the Environment, 27 October, Durham.

Bell, D. (2005) 'Liberal environmental citizenship', *Environmental Politics*, vol. 14, no. 2, pp. 179–94.

Bentham, J. (1996 [1789]) 'An introduction to the principles of morals and legislation' in Burns, J. H. and Hart, H. L. A. (eds) *Collected Works of Jeremy Bentham*, Oxford, Oxford University Press.

Caney, S. (2001) 'International distributive justice', *Political Studies*, vol. 49, no. 5, pp. 974–7.

Connelly, J. (2006) 'The virtues of environmental citizenship' in Dobson and Bell (eds) (2006).

Devall, B. and Sessions, G. (2000 [1985]) 'Deep ecology' in Benton, L. M. and Short, J. R. (eds) *Environmental Discourse and Practice: A Reader*, Oxford, Blackwell Publishing.

Dobson, A. (2003) *Citizenship and the Environment*, Oxford, Oxford University Press.

Dobson, A. and Bell, D. (eds) (2006) *Environmental Citizenship*, Cambridge, MA, MIT Press.

Hobbes, T. (1991 [1651]) *Leviathan* (ed. R. Tuck), Cambridge, Cambridge University Press.

Hursthouse, R. (1998) 'Applying virtue ethics' in Hursthouse, R., Lawrence, G. and Quinn, W. (eds) *Virtues and Reasons: Philippa Foot and Moral Theory*, Oxford, Clarendon Press.

Kant, I. (2005 [1785]) *Groundwork of the Metaphysics of Morals* (ed. L. Denis), Calgary, AB, Broadview Press.

Leydet, D. (2008) 'Citizenship' in Zalta, E. N. (ed.) *Stanford Encyclopedia of Philosophy* [online], http://plato.stanford.edu/archives/Fall2008/entries/citizenship (Accessed 19 December 2008).

Linklater, A. (1998) *The Transformation of Political Community: Ethical Foundations of the Post-Westphalian Era*, Cambridge, Polity Press.

Locke, J. (1988 [1690]) *Two Treatises of Government* (ed. P. Laslett), Cambridge, Cambridge University Press.

Mill, J. S. (1977 [1859]) 'Thoughts on parliamentary reform' (ed. J. M. Robson), *The Collected Works of John Stuart Mill, vol. XIX: Essays on Politics and Society Part 2*, London, Routledge.

Nash, R. F. (1989) *The Rights of Nature: A History of Environmental Ethics*, Wisconsin, WI, University of Wisconsin Press.

Pangsapa, P. and Smith, M. J. (2009) *Responsible Politics: Bringing Together Labor Standards, Environment and Human Rights*, New York, Palgrave Macmillan.

Rousseau, J. -J. (1997 [1762]) *The Social Contract and Other Later Political Writings* (ed. V. Gourevitch), Cambridge, Cambridge University Press.

Schlosberg, D. (2007) *Defining Environmental Justice: Theories, Movements and Nature*, Oxford, Oxford University Press.

Seyfang, G. (2005) 'Shopping for sustainability: can sustainable consumption promote ecological citizenship?', *Environmental Politics*, vol. 14, no. 2, pp. 290–306.

Seyfang, G. (2006) 'Ecological citizenship and sustainable consumption: examining local organic food networks', *Journal of Rural Studies*, vol. 22, no. 4, pp. 383–95.

Singer, P. (1976) *Animal Liberation: Towards an End to Man's Inhumanity to Animals*, Wellingborough, Thorsons.

Smith, M. J. and Pangsapa, P. (2008) *Environment and Citizenship: Integrating Justice, Responsibility and Civic Engagement*, London, Zed Books.

Smith, M. J. and Pangsapa, P. (2009) 'Strategic thinking and the practices of ecological citizenship' in Reynolds, M., Blackmore, C. and Smith, M. J. (eds) *Environmental Responsibility*, London, Zed Books.

Acknowledgements

Grateful acknowledgement is made to the following sources:

Figures

Figure 1.1: Copyright © Graham Spillard www.spockman.com; Figure 1.2: Copyright © Yann Arthus-Bertrand/Corbis; Figure 1.4a: Copyright © Louise Gubb/Corbis; Figure 1.5b: Copyright © Anna Zieminski/Getty Images; Figure 1.5 top: Copyright © Vanderlei Almeida/AFP/Getty Images; Figure 1.5 bottom: Copyright © Stephanie Maze/Corbis; Figure 1.6: Copyright © UPPA/Photoshot; Figure 1.7a: Copyright © David Jay Zimmermann/Corbis; Figure 1.7b: Copyright © UPPA/Photoshot Photo CPH 077879 01.05.1979; Figure 1.8: Global Environment Outlook (2007) Geo 4 Environment for Development, UNEP; Figure 1.10: Copyright © Fran Orford; Figure 1.11 bottom: Courtesy of Adbusters Media Foundation; Figure 2.1: Copyright © Paul Langrock/Zenit/Greenpeace; Figure 2.2 top: Copyright © Bettmann/Corbis; Figure 2.2 bottom: Copyright © Gene Herrick/AP/PA Photos; Figure 2.3: Copyright © Jonathan McIntosh; Figure 2.4: Woodland Trust; Figure 2.5: Copyright © Elizabeth Botkin, courtesy of Sea Shepherd Conservation Society; Figure 2.6: Copyright © Jenny Labalme; Figure 2.7 left: Copyright © The Eng Koon/AFP/Getty Images; Figure 2.7 right: Copyright © China Daily Information Copr CDIC/Reuters; Figure 2.8: Copyright © Natalie Behring/Greenpeace; Figure 2.10: Copyright © Manit Sriwanichpoom; Figure 3.1 top left: Copyright © S Chamnanrith/UNEP/Still Pictures; Figure 3.1 top right: Copyright © Karen Robinson/Panos Pictures; Figure 3.1 bottom right: Copyright © Pavel Rahman/AP/PA Photos; Figure 3.1 bottom left: Copyright © Ricardo Beliel/Still Pictures; Figure 3.2: Copyright © Ed Kashi/Corbis; Figure 3.3: Copyright © ITV/Rex Features; Figure 3.4: Copyright © Mike Kolloffel/Still Pictures; Figure 3.5: Copyright © Biosphoto/Lorgnier Antoine/Still Pictures; Figure 3.6: Copyright © Arco Images GmbH/Alamy; Figure 3.7: Copyright © Tibor Bognar/Alamy; Figure 3.8 top: Copyright © Karen Robinson/Panos; Figure 3.8 centre: Copyright © Kapoor Baldev/Sygma/Corbis; Figure 3.8 bottom: Copyright © Kamal Kishore/Reuters/Corbis; Figure 3.9: Copyright © Karen Robinson/Panos; Figure 3.10 top: Copyright © Florian Kopp/Imagebroker/FLPA; Figure 3.10 bottom: Copyright © Robert Harding Picture Library Ltd/Alamy Images; Figure 4.1 top left: Copyright © Thierry Roge/Reuters; Figure 4.1 top centre: Copyright © Andreas Gebert/vario images GmbH & Co KG/Alamy; Figure 4.1 top right: Copyright © Michel Springler/AP/PA Photos; Figure 4.1 bottom left: Copyright © Thierry Tronnel/Corbis; Figure 4.1 bottom right: Copyright © Jean-Christophe Verhaegen/Getty Images; Figure 4.3: Courtesy of the Office for Official Publications of the European Communities; Figure 4.5: Copyright © Kristine Linda/ Alamy Images; Figure 4.6: Copyright © David Musial and Jana Dostalova; Figure 5.1: Copyright © Bettmann/Corbis; Figure 5.2: Copyright © Mary Evans Picture Library; Figure 5.3 left: Copyright © Mary Evans Picture Library/Rue des Archives/PVDE; Figure 5.3 right: Copyright © Bettmann/Corbis; Figure 5.4: Smith, M.J. and Pangsapa, P. (2008) Environment and Citizenship: Integrating Justice, Responsibility and Civic Engagement, Zed Books.

Every effort has been made to locate all copyright-owners, but if any have been overlooked the publishers will make the necessary arrangements at the first opportunity.

Index